© 1960

Dale Maley

WAVE PROPAGATION AND GROUP VELOCITY

PURE AND APPLIED PHYSICS

A SERIES OF MONOGRAPHS AND TEXTBOOKS

CONSULTING EDITOR

H. S. W. MASSEY

University College, London, England

Volume 1. F. H. FIELD and J. L. FRANKLIN, Electron Impact Phenomena and the Properties of Gaseous Ions. 1957

Volume 2. H. KOPFERMANN, Nuclear Moments. English Version Prepared from the Second German Edition by E. E. SCHNEIDER. 1958

Volume 3. WALTER E. THIRRING, Principles of Quantum Electrodynamics. Translated from the German by J. BERNSTEIN. With Corrections and Additions by WALTER E. THIRRING. 1958

Volume 4. U. FANO and G. RACAH, Irreducible Tensorial Sets. 1959

Volume 5. E. P. WIGNER, Group Theory and Its Application to the Quantum Mechanics of Atomic Spectra. Expanded and Improved Edition. Translated from the German by J. J. GRIFFIN. 1959

Volume 6. J. IRVING and N. MULLINEUX, Mathematics in Physics and Engineering. 1959

Volume 7. KARL F. HERZFELD and THEODORE A. LITOVITZ, Absorption and Dispersion of Ultrasonic Waves. 1959

Volume 8. LEON BRILLOUIN, Wave Propagation and Group Velocity. 1960

IN PREPARATION

FAY AJZENBERG-SELOVE (ed.), Nuclear Spectroscopy. In two parts.

DAVID R. BATES (ed.), Quantum Theory. In three parts.

ACADEMIC PRESS • *New York and London*

WAVE PROPAGATION
AND
GROUP VELOCITY

LÉON BRILLOUIN
Member of the National Academy of Sciences

1960

ACADEMIC PRESS New York and London

ACADEMIC PRESS INC.
111 FIFTH AVENUE
NEW YORK 3, N. Y.

United Kingdom Edition
Published by
ACADEMIC PRESS INC. (LONDON) LTD.
40 PALL MALL, LONDON S.W. 1

Library of Congress Catalog Card Number 59-13829

PRINTED IN THE UNITED STATES OF AMERICA

FOREWORD

Munich, in the spring 1913, was a very lively city with a famous University, and the Institute for Theoretical Physics of this University had won a high reputation under the leadership of Professor A. Sommerfeld. This young professor had already achieved great fame. He had published a remarkable book on the theory of the gyroscope, and had presented a very extraordinary paper at the first Solvay Congress in *Brussels in 1911* [French edition at Gauthier-Villars, Paris 1912, p. 316 and p. 403]. In a stroke of genius, he noted that Planck's constant h represented a *quantum of action,* and that the familiar quantum of energy $h\nu$ was only an indirect result of quantizing the action. He made a few curious applications of this revolutionary idea, which P. Langevin immediately used to compute a *magneton,* which differed from the present Bohr magneton only by a factor 2π.

When Bohr's paper on the hydrogen atom was published in 1913, Sommerfeld immediately saw the importance of this new idea. I happened to be in his office when he opened the issue of the *Philosophical Magazine,* which had just arrived; he glanced through it and told me: "There is a most important paper here by N. Bohr, it will mark a date in theoretical physics." And soon after, Sommerfeld started applying his own "quantum of action" method to rebuild a consistent theory of Bohr's atom. This is how the first quantized mechanics was born, and why it progressed so fast. It was definitely Sommerfeld's discovery of the importance of the $\int p dq$ integrals that paved the way and these integrals still are at the basis of the whole quantum theory.

Everybody wondered (and still wonders) why the Stockholm committee systematically ignored Sommerfeld's pioneer work in modern physics. Such an omission is actually impossible to understand.

My friend P. P. Ewald gave an excellent summary of Sommerfeld's achievements, and described the life at the Munich Institute for Theoretical Physics, in a Foreword to Volume I of Sommerfeld's lectures ("Mechanics,"Academic Press, 1952). The special clarity and the mathematical accuracy of Sommerfeld's lectures were really remarkable. I had the great privilege of attending, as a student, lectures given by some prominent physicists, such as H. A. Lorentz, H. Poincaré, and P. Langevin. But I was especially impressed by Sommerfeld's mastery as a teacher. In his Foreword to Volume I, Ewald quotes a few problems in which Sommerfeld was interested in 1913. Among them is the question of signal velocity in a dispersive medium, a short summary of which is presented in Volume 5, § 22. This was the subject of research suggested to me by Sommerfeld and it resulted in twin papers published by us in the *Annalen der Physik* of 1914. The subject was a fascinating one, but it had, at that time, only academic importance. Experimental verifications were discovered much later, in connection with reflections of radio signals from the Heaviside layers, and also for problems of radar systems. Theoretical applications suddenly appeared with wave mechanics, when Schrödinger discovered that group velocity should be identified with the velocity of particles guided by the waves.

All these modern developments made it advisable to assemble here a systematic presentation of the original papers, which are rather difficult to find nowadays. It is hoped that the present book will be helpful to many readers and save them time and trouble, especially the trouble of recomputing and rediscovering many important features of the general theory.

It is a pleasant duty to thank Dr. E. Erlbach of the Watson Laboratory for preparing translations of the German and French papers.

L. Brillouin

New York
September, 1959

PREFACE

When a mathematician thinks of wave propagation, he starts by writing a well-known second order differential equation and discussing its peculiar properties. The physicist is interested in these results, but he immediately asks some indiscreet questions about waves in a dispersive medium, when the velocity of propagation is not a constant, but strongly depends upon the frequency. The well-known differential equation is no longer satisfied and must be replaced by a more complicated system of equations, which include the model, the physical mechanism, reacting on the waves and modifying the velocity. Each problem seems different, but nevertheless some general properties may be deduced and some definitions can be found to apply to a wide class of systems.

One of the most important definitions refers to the *group velocity*. It seems to have been first discovered by Lord Rayleigh, who characterized this velocity in sound waves. It is now known to apply to practically all kinds of waves. Let us use the vocabulary of radio engineers and consider a carrier wave, with a superimposed modulation. The *phase velocity* yields the motion of elementary wavelets in the carrier, while the group velocity gives the propagation of the modulation. Lord Rayleigh considered that the group velocity corresponds to the velocity of energy or signals.

This however raised difficulties with the theory of relativity which states that no velocity can be higher than c, the velocity of light in vacuum. Group velocity, as originally defined, became larger than c or even negative within an absorption band. Such a contradiction had to be resolved and was extensively discussed in many meetings about 1910. Sommerfeld stated the problem correctly and proved that no signal velocity could exceed c. I discussed the solution in great detail and gave a complete answer. These original papers and discussions are presented in the first chapters of this book. It was found desirable to reprint completely these papers, which were published during the First World War and are missing in many libraries.

In the following chapters we give a later discussion of the subject, and introduce three different definitions of velocities: A — the *group velocity* of Lord Rayleigh; B — the *signal velocity* of Sommerfeld; C — the *velocity of energy transfer*, which yields the rate of energy flow through a continuous wave and is strongly related to the characteristic impedance.

These three velocities are identical for nonabsorbing media, but they differ considerably in an absorption band.

Some examples are discussed in the last chapter dealing with guided waves, and many other cases of application of these definitions are quoted.

These problems have come again into the foreground, in connection with the propagation of radio signals and radar. Reflection in the Heaviside layers requires a real knowledge of all these different definitions. Group velocity also plays a very important role in wave mechanics and corresponds to the speed of a particle.

The present book should be very useful to physicists and radio engineers and should give them a good basis for new discussions and applications.

L. Brillouin

New York
September, 1959

CONTENTS

CHAPTER I

INTRODUCTION

1. Phase Velocity and Group Velocity

Many modern ideas on wave propagation originated in the famous works of Lord Rayleigh, and the problems we intend to discuss are no exception to this rule. The distinction between phase velocity and group velocity appears very early in Rayleigh's papers.[1] It can be found in his "Theory of Sound"[2] and in many articles reprinted in his "Scientific Papers." The problem is discussed in particular in connection with measurements of the velocity of light;[3] and this is the place where a curious error was introduced regarding the angle of aberration. We shall come back to this point later when discussing a very important paper by P. Ehrenfest (see Section 5 of this chapter).

Let us first remind the reader of the fact that the usual velocity W of waves is defined as giving the phase difference between the vibrations observed at two different points in a free plane wave. It is primarily used for computing interference fringes that make phase differences visible. In a wave

$$\psi = A \cos (\omega t - kx) = A \cos \omega \left(t - \frac{x}{W}\right) \tag{1}$$

we observe the *phase velocity* W

$$W = \frac{\omega}{k} \tag{2}$$

---

[1] The very first idea of group velocity appears in a paper by W. R. Hamilton, *Proc. Roy. Irish Acad.* **1**, 267, **341** (1839).

[2] Lord Rayleigh, "Theory of Sound," 2nd ed. (1894). First ed. published, 1877.

[3] Lord Rayleigh, "Scientific Papers," Vol. I, p. 537. 1881.

Another velocity can be defined, if we consider the propagation of a peculiarity (to use Rayleigh's term), that is, of a change in amplitude impressed on a train of waves.

This is what we now call a *modulation* impressed on a *carrier*. The modulation results in the building up of some "groups" of large amplitude (Rayleigh) which move along with the *group velocity* U. In wave mechanics, Schrödinger called these groups "*wave-packets.*" A simple combination of groups obtains when two waves

$$\omega_1 = \omega + \Delta\omega \qquad k_1 = k + \Delta k$$
$$\omega_2 = \omega - \Delta\omega \qquad k_2 = k - \Delta k \tag{3}$$

are superimposed, giving:

$$\begin{aligned}\psi &= A\cos(\omega_1 t - k_1 x) + A\cos(\omega_2 t - k_2 x)\\ &= 2A\cos(\omega t - kx)\cos(\Delta\omega t - \Delta k x)\end{aligned} \tag{4}$$

This represents a carrier with frequency ω and a modulation with frequency $\Delta\omega$. The wave may be described as a succession of moving beats (or groups, or wave-packets). The carrier's velocity is W [Eq. (2)], while the group velocity is given by U

$$U = \frac{\Delta\omega}{\Delta k} \to \frac{\partial\omega}{\partial k} \quad \text{for} \quad \Delta k \to 0 \tag{5}$$

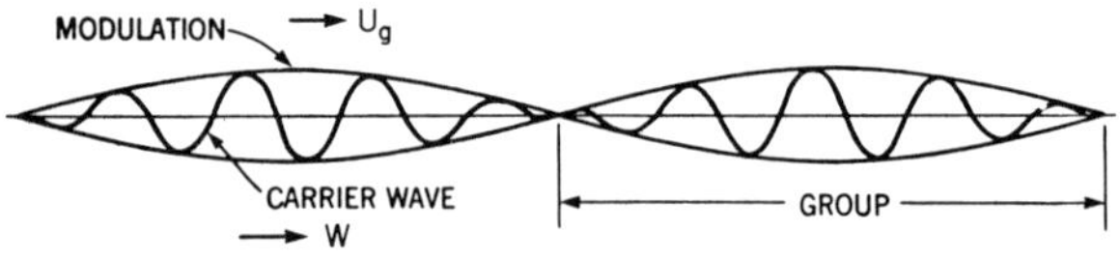

FIG. 1.

The situation is represented in Fig. 1 where we see a succession of wavelets (ω,k) with variable amplitude ($\Delta\omega$, Δk). If we do not pay attention to the detailed motion and observe only the average amplitude distribution, we verify that the amplitude curve moves forward with the group velocity U. Looking more carefully at the detailed vibrations, we may see the wavelets moving within the envelope with their own velocity W. We distinguish two different cases:

(6) $U > W$ The wavelets are building up in front of the group and disappearing in the rear end of the group.

(7) $U < W$ The wavelets are building up at the back end of the group, progressing through the group, and disappearing in the front.

2. Examples and Discussion: Dispersive Media

In a medium where the phase velocity W is a constant and does not depend upon frequency, we have

$$U = W \tag{8}$$

and any kind of signal is propagated without distortion.

More generally, when W is a function of ω (or k), we have

$$U = \frac{\partial \omega}{\partial k}$$

with $\omega = kW$, hence:

$$U = W + k\frac{\partial W}{\partial k} \tag{9a}$$

This is often written with the wave length λ as variable instead of k, when $k = 2\pi/\lambda$; hence,

$$U = W - \lambda\frac{\partial W}{\partial \lambda} \tag{9b}$$

A medium exhibiting a wave velocity $W(k)$ is called a dispersive medium. Vacuum is nondispersive for light ($W = U = c$), but all material media are dispersive. It is impossible to think of a refractive medium without dispersion. The situation is even more complicated, since W depends upon the variables λ (or ω), the density ρ, and the temperature T. In crystals, the direction of propagation is also to be taken into account. We shall restrict our discussions to isotropic media, but we must assume

$$W = W(k,\rho,T) \tag{10}$$

This is where the physicist's viewpoint differs from the mathematician's idealization. Many textbooks on electromagnetic theory discuss material media with

(11) $\varepsilon \geqslant \varepsilon_0$ dielectric constants of matter and vacuum
$\mu \geqslant \mu_0$ permeabilities of matter and vacuum

but they usually assume ε and μ to be constant, and this is a physical impossibility. The complete problem dealing with the three variables k, ρ T will be examined in Chapter V.

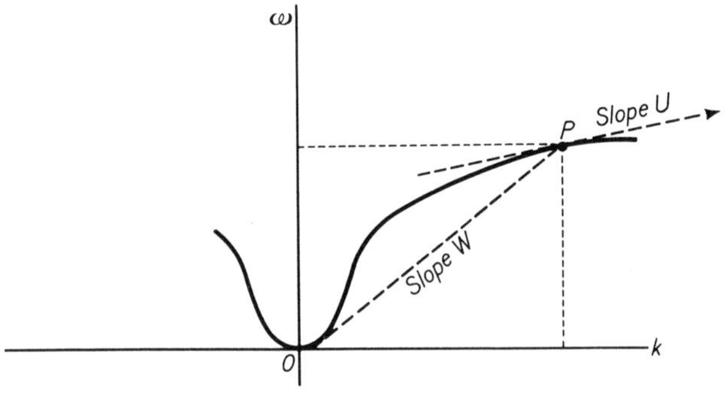

FIG. 2.

A very useful graphical representation obtains if we plot ω as a function of k (Fig. 2). The slope of the chord OP gives the phase velocity W, while the slope of the tangent at point P yields the group velocity U.

The velocity of *light* is a constant in vacuum, but depends upon frequency in material media. The velocity of *sound* is approximately constant for long wavelengths, but depends strongly on the frequency at short wavelengths, especially when the wavelength is of the order of the distance between molecules. Many such examples have been discussed in the literature.[4] The group velocity for sound is then equal to the phase velocity only for long wavelengths.

It was assumed, at the beginning, that the group velocity was actually the velocity at which a finite signal may propagate through the medium, but this is only an approximation. We shall see later that a finite signal is distorted while traveling through the medium, and that its velocity may become very hard to define, on account of the change in the shape.

This is especially true for an absorbing medium. Absorption is strongly frequency dependent, and is always associated with strong dispersion.

As a rule, we shall see that the velocity of a signal does not differ too much from the group velocity, whenever absorption and dispersion are small. Otherwise, the velocities may differ widely.

Let us now discuss a few interesting examples, to which the reader may add a great variety of problems discussed by L. Brillouin in a previous book.[4]

Rayleigh discusses[5] the problem of wave propagation along a bar, and obtains an equation for lateral vibrations:

$$\frac{\partial^2 y}{\partial t^2} + K^2 b^2 \frac{\partial^4 y}{\partial x^4} = 0 \tag{12}$$

This propagation is frequency dependent, and for a wavelength λ one obtains a velocity

$$W = \frac{2\pi K b}{\lambda} = Kbk \tag{13}$$

with $k = 2\pi/\lambda$.

In this example, Rayleigh discusses the problem of group velocity. He assumes, more generally,

$$W = B\lambda^n = B'k^{-n} \tag{14}$$

---

[4] See, for instance: L. Brillouin, "Wave Propagation in Periodic Structures." McGraw-Hill, New York, 1946. Reprinted, Dover, New York, 1953. L. Brillouin and M. Parodi, "Propagation des ondes dans les milieux périodiques." Masson, Paris, 1956.

[5] Lord Rayleigh, reference 2, Vol. I, Section 191, p. 301.

which results, by our formulas (8) or (9), in

$$U = W(1 - n) \tag{15}$$

For lateral vibrations of *bars*,

$$n = -1 \qquad U = 2W \tag{16}$$

The group velocity is thus twice as large as the phase velocity. This is a typical example of case (7) in Section 1 above.

In another chapter of "Theory of Sound,"[6] Rayleigh discusses surface waves on water. Assuming a density ρ, a depth l, gravity g, and surface tension T, he obtains the general formula for the phase velocity[7]

$$W^2 = \frac{g}{k} + \frac{Tk}{\rho} \tanh(kl) \tag{17}$$

a formula exhibiting a strong dependence on k.

In many important cases, the depth l can be considered as practically infinite (deep water waves); thus the hyperbolic tangent is 1, and hence

$$W^2 = \frac{g}{k} + \frac{Tk}{\rho} \qquad k = \frac{2\pi}{\lambda} \tag{18}$$

When λ is great, k is small, and the waves move mainly under gravity, with a velocity

$$W = \left(\frac{g}{k}\right)^{1/2} \quad \text{when} \quad k^2 \ll \frac{g\rho}{T}, \qquad \lambda^2 \gg \frac{4\pi^2 T}{g\rho} \tag{19}$$

This is the case of long waves on deep sea. For small ripples, k is large, the second term in Eq. (18) is dominant, and

$$W = \left(\frac{Tk}{\rho}\right)^{1/2} \tag{20}$$

---

[6] Lord Rayleigh, reference 2, Vol. II, Chapter XX.

[7] Lord Rayleigh, reference 2, Vol. II, p. 344, Eq. (7).

Between these extreme cases, there is a minimum velocity W_0 corresponding to λ_0 and τ_0 values for wavelength and period, respectively.

$$(21) \qquad W_0 = \left(\frac{4Tg}{\rho}\right)^{1/4} \qquad \lambda_0 = 2\pi\left(\frac{T}{g\rho}\right)^{1/2} \qquad \tau_0 = 2\pi\left(\frac{T}{4g^3\rho}\right)^{1/4}$$

According to Eq. (19), *long waves on deep sea* yield a power of $n = \frac{1}{2}$ and hence a group velocity

$$(22) \qquad U = \frac{1}{2} W$$

according to Eq. (15). This is a typical example of case (6) in Section 1 above.

Short ripples moving under *surface tension*, on the contrary, correspond to $n = -\frac{1}{2}$ in Eq. (20); hence

$$(23) \qquad U = \frac{3}{2} W$$

which is an example of case (7).

A very simple experiment can easily be made and provides an excellent example of group velocity. Just throw a stone in a pond, and look at the "rings" produced on the surface. They are composed of a small number of short ripples. The system as a whole propagates with the group velocity U but each individual ripple moves with the phase velocity W. Since $W < U$, these ripples are building up along the outside ring, moving more slowly than the ring, and disappearing on the inside of the ring.

3. Groups and Signals

The preceding example may serve as an introduction to the discussion of signals. *Groups* were defined by Rayleigh as moving beats [Eqs. (4) and (5)] following each other in a regular pattern. A *signal* is a short isolated succession of wavelets, with the system at rest before the signal arrived and also after it has passed. A signal may be sharply defined in time and duration, in which case its frequency spectrum extends from $-\infty$ to $+\infty$, or it may have a finite spectrum, and exhibit no absolutely sharp boundaries. These problems were extensively discussed elsewhere.[8]

We shall assume a signal carried by a *carrier-frequency* ω_0 and characterized by a *modulation* curve $C(t)$. The complete signal sent along the line at the input $x = 0$ is

$$C_1(t,0) = C(t)\cos\omega_0 t \tag{24}$$

Let us now analyze the *modulation* $C(t)$ in a Fourier integral, assuming that this modulation has a finite spectrum extending from 0 to ω_m:

$$C(t) = \int_{\omega=0}^{\omega_m} B_\omega \cos(\omega t + \phi_\omega)\,d\omega \tag{25}$$

where B_ω is the amplitude and ϕ_ω the phase of the ω component. The input signal [Eq. (24)] is represented by the Fourier integral

$$\begin{aligned} C_1(t,0) &= \int_{\omega=0}^{\omega_m} B_\omega \cos(\omega t + \phi_\omega)\cos(\omega_0 t)\,d\omega \\ &= \frac{1}{2}\int_{\omega=0}^{\omega_m} B_\omega\{\cos[(\omega_0+\omega)t+\phi_\omega] + \cos[(\omega_0-\omega)t-\phi_0]\}\,d\omega \end{aligned} \tag{26}$$

The resulting spectrum now extends from $(\omega_0 - \omega_m)$ to $(\omega_0 + \omega_m)$ and thus covers a band $2\omega_m$. For simplicity's sake, we may assume

$$\omega_0 \geqslant \omega_m \tag{27}$$

and avoid negative frequencies. The line along which propagation occurs is characterized by a certain relation between ω and k, as visualized in Fig. 2.

---

[8] L. Brillouin, reference 4, Chapter V, p. 78. L. Brillouin and M. Parodi, reference 4, Chapter V, p. 81. L. Brillouin, "Science and Information Theory," Chapter 8, p. 86. Academic Press, New York, 1956.

Let us now assume a simplified problem, exemplified in Fig. 3. This problem was stated by Schuster[9] and represents a limiting case for many actual problems. The assumption is that

(28) $$W = a + b\lambda = a + \frac{2\pi b}{k}$$

in which a and b are constants; hence

(29) $$\omega = Wk = ak + 2\pi b$$
$$U = \frac{\partial \omega}{\partial k} = a$$

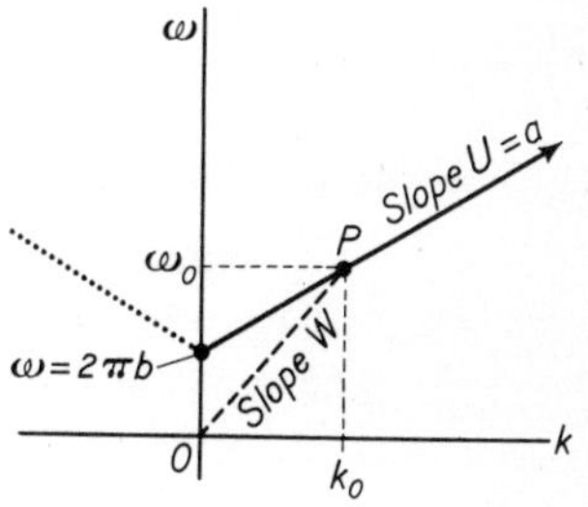

FIG. 3.

a constant.

The quantity k is supposed to be positive, but negative values would yield the dotted curve of Fig. 3. We now have to sharpen condition (27), assuming that

(30) $$\omega_0 - \omega_m \geqslant 2\pi b$$

since the line does not transmit frequencies below $2\pi b$. With this model, we have the following situation:

(31) the carrier frequency ω_0 corresponds to k_0.
a frequency $\omega_0 + \omega$ corresponds to $k_0 + (\omega/U)$.

We now can rebuild the signal as it arrives at point x, simply by replacing, in Eq. (26), $\omega_0 t$ by $(\omega_0 t - k_0 x)$ and $(\omega_0 + \omega)t$ by $(\omega_0 + \omega)t - [k_0 + (\omega/U)]x$.

This transformation yields:

(32) $$C_1(t,x) = \frac{1}{2}\int_{\omega=0}^{\omega_m} B_\omega[\cos(\theta_0 + \theta) + \cos(\theta_0 - \theta)]\,d\omega$$
$$= \cos\theta_0 \int B_\omega \cos\theta\,d\omega = \cos\theta_0 C\left(t - \frac{x}{U}\right)$$

---

[9] A. Schuster, "Boltzmann Festschrift," p. 569. 1904.

with $\theta_0 = \omega_0 t - k_0 x$ and $\theta_\omega = \omega[t - (x/U)] + \phi_\omega$. The last transformation results directly from Eq. (25). Finally, the signal reaching the distance x is given by

$$C_1(t,x) = C\left(t - \frac{x}{U}\right)\cos\omega_0\left(t - \frac{x}{W}\right) \tag{33}$$

and we have proved, for the Schuster model, the following points:

(a). The *modulation* $C[t - (x/U)]$ is propagated without any distortion, and yields the *group velocity* U.

(b). The carrier ω_0 exhibits its own phase velocity W.

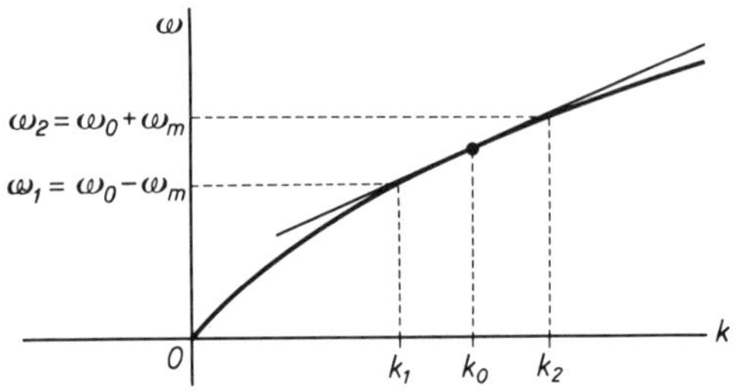

FIG. 4.

In the Schuster example, the signal velocity is a constant, exactly equal to the group velocity. This is, however, an oversimplified model. A more realistic case corresponds to the situation sketched in Figs. (2) and (4). Here, the preceding result is only a *first* approximation, valid only if it is possible to replace the curve by its tangent over the frequency band $(\omega_0 \pm \omega_m)$ around the carrier frequency ω_0.

In general, the signal velocity will differ from the group velocity, especially if the phase velocity is strongly frequency-dependent and if the absorption cannot be ignored (as it was in the Schuster model).

4. Signal Velocity, First Attempts

Some earlier authors managed to take one step farther, and to obtain examples in which the signal velocity S could be compared to the group velocity U. W. Voigt[10] studied very carefully the properties of the telegraphists' equation

$$\frac{\partial^2 \psi}{\partial t^2} = c^2 \frac{\partial^2 \psi}{\partial x^2} - \omega_0 \frac{\partial \psi}{\partial t} \tag{34}$$

and he was able to show that the velocity of the front of the disturbance is smaller than the group velocity. The *front* is defined as a surface beyond which, at a given instant of time, the medium is completely at rest. Voigt's result proves definitely that there must be a distinction between *signal* and *group* velocity. We shall even have to distinguish between the front velocity and the signal velocity. Front velocity will correspond to the speed at which the very first, extremely small (perhaps invisible) vibrations will occur, while the signal velocity yields the arrival of the main signal, with intensities of the order of magnitude of the input signal.

P. Ehrenfest[11] obtains results similar to those of Voigt on a different equation

$$\frac{\partial^2 \psi}{\partial t^2} = \alpha^2 \frac{\partial^2 \psi}{\partial x^2} + \beta^2 \psi \tag{35}$$

This would correspond to a string, pushed away from its equilibrium position by a force $\beta^2 \psi$. The system is unstable; a disturbance propagates with the front velocity α and increases progressively in amplitude. Infinitely long sine waves propagate without amplitude change, and exhibit a phase velocity

$$W = \alpha \left(1 - \frac{\lambda^2 \beta^2}{4\pi^2 \alpha^2}\right)^{1/2} < \alpha \tag{36}$$

hence a group velocity

$$UW = \alpha^2 \qquad U = \frac{\alpha}{\left(1 - \dfrac{\lambda^2 \beta^2}{4\pi^2 \alpha^2}\right)^{1/2}} > \alpha \tag{37}$$

---

[10] W. Voigt, *Ann. Physik* [3] **68**, 598 (1899); [4] **4**, 203 (1901).

[11] P. Ehrenfest, *Ann. Physik* [4] **33**, 1571 (1910).

and the group velocity is larger than the front velocity α. Many other examples of greater importance for the physicist will be discussed in the following chapters.

A. Sommerfeld[12] started a very fundamental discussion when he compared the theory of signal propagation with the relativistic statement that no signal, no particle can move faster than c, the velocity of light in vacuum. This point required an explanation, since the laws of dispersion in refractive media yield, in a region of anomalous dispersion, velocities W and U that may become larger than c. Sommerfeld immediately noted that the group velocity U cannot represent the velocity S of a signal, especially in a frequency region where the frequency dependence is high and absorption is strong.

In this short note, Sommerfeld sketched briefly the general mathematical method which he invented for this discussion, and which will be given in details in the following chapter. He could immediately show that no signal can move faster than c and that actually the *front* of the signal was progressing with the velocity c through the dispersive medium. Let us quote:

"It can be proven that the signal velocity is exactly equal to c, if we assume the observer to be equipped with a detector of infinite sensivity, and this is true for normal or anomalous dispersion, for isotropic or anisotropic medium, that may or may not contain conduction electrons. The signal velocity has absolutely nothing to do with the phase velocity. There is nothing, in this problem, in the way of Relativity theory."

The theory shows that the signal is very strongly distorted. The medium is initially at rest, then the front appears with velocity c, but this front corresponds to infinitely small fields and electronic motions. Both fields and electronic motions build up progressively, but Sommerfeld did not obtain the complete shape of this complicated signal distortion. Thus the mathematical theory was given a very precise formulation, but the physical picture remained rather mysterious, as was proved in the discussion following the paper. The

---

[12] A. Sommerfeld, Ein Einwand gegen die Relativtheorie der Elektrodynamik und seine Beseitigung. *Physik. Z.* **8**, 841 (1907). (Vorträge von der 79. Naturforscherversammlung zu Dresden.)

complete physical explanation came later in this discussion and was given by Voigt. It is worth quoting almost literally:

"The modern theory of dispersion and absorption uses the assumption of point electrons having a finite mass, and distributed in the (so-called) ether. The assumption of an inertial mass results immediately in the fact that these particles can in no way react upon the beginning of a wave. It is only after the wave is started that the electrons are set in motion and react on the wave. Accordingly, I am not at all surprised with Sommerfeld's result, that the front of the wave always travels with the velocity *c* of light in vacuum."

This explanation was obviously suggested by the very important results obtained by Voigt in his previous work, which was quoted at the beginning of this section.

Wien added, in conclusion to this meeting, that he would like very much to know the shape of the whole signal. This is what we are going to discuss in the following chapters.

5. Actual Measurements of the Velocity of Light

It was recognized by Rayleigh that all experimental methods for measuring the velocity of light did operate with light signals, and hence did not measure the phase velocity but the signal velocity, and this velocity was assumed to coincide with the group velocity. We do not intend to discuss here the well-known experiments of Römer, Fizeau, or Foucault. The reader may find all the necessary explanation in Sommerfeld's lectures on optics.[13] In Römer's method, the signals are defined by the rotation of Jupiter's satellite, and in the other methods, the signals result from the rotating mirror or the rotating toothed wheel.

The significance of the measurement of a parallax is not so obvious. Rayleigh first assumed that it was related to phase velocity, but this statement was later corrected by Ehrenfest.[11,14]

---

[13] A. Sommerfeld, "Optics," Chapter II, pp. 60–75. Academic Press, New York, 1954.

[14] T. H. Havelock, "The Propagation of Disturbances in Dispersive Media." Cambridge Tract in Math. and Phys. No. 17. Cambridge Univ. Press, London, 1914.

Figure 5 explains the situation, assuming a simplified device consisting of two parallel plates moving with a uniform velocity v in the horizontal direction. Monochromatic light is falling normally on the first plate and generates an oblique ray. It is obvious that the obliquity is determined by the signal (or group) velocity of the finite signals making up the ray. Altogether, the experiment is fundamentally similar to the Fizeau procedure. Both of them can only measure the signal velocity, which is practically the group velocity.

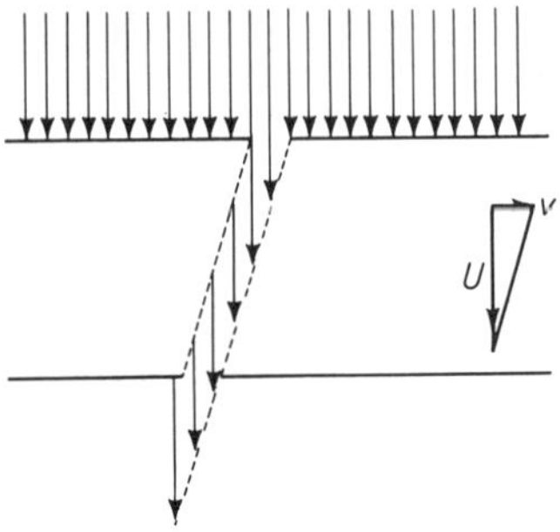

FIG. 5.

6. Havelock's Pamphlet

A general review of the situation was published in 1914 by T. H. Havelock.[14] It contains a very extensive bibliography of earlier publications, up to the first paper by Sommerfeld. Let us note, for instance, an illuminating discussion of *Kelvin's method of stationary phase*: if we have a Fourier decomposition of the propagating signal

$$y = \int_0^\infty A \cos k(x - Wt)\, dk \tag{38}$$

we may find positions and times at which a large number of components have the same phase and reinforce each other. They will thus produce the predominant part of the signal, while other elements are practically destroyed by interferences. This leads to the condition

$$\frac{d\phi}{dk} = \frac{d}{dk} k(x - Wt) = 0 \tag{39}$$

or,

$$x - Ut = 0 \qquad \text{where} \qquad U = \frac{d}{dk}(kW)$$

U is the group velocity previously defined. The approximate shape of the dominant group in the signal can be computed. This method was repeatedly used by Lord Kelvin and proved very powerful in many problems. One drawback is that it requires W to be real (*no absorption*). When there is absorption, the method must be replaced by the more general "saddle point method," as we shall see in Chapter III.

Havelock gives interesting discussions of a variety of special examples, and often succeeds in obtaining simple solutions. He has a number of problems in which a short pulse is the initial signal; he then computes the progressive distortion of the signal for different types of propagation. Similar discussions regained a great deal of importance later in connection with wave-mechanical problems, in which a "group" or "wavepacket" was taken as representing a particle, and group velocity was identified with particle speed. Havelock systematically uses the Cornu spiral to build some solutions of waves on water and presents a number of interesting examples from Lord Kelvin and Green.

There is also, in Havelock's book, an interesting chapter on *energy flow*, with the modern definition of a *velocity of energy transfer*, illustrated by examples of vibrations of springs, waves on water, and electromagnetic waves.

These problems shall be discussed in Chapter IV; other examples are found in the books quoted under reference 4.

7. General Remarks

The preceding sections summarize the situation in about 1910 when Sommerfeld started discussing the problem and attempted to apply the general method sketched in Section 4 of this chapter. We noted the interest in the problem, and how a galaxy of eminent scientists, from Voigt to Einstein, attached great importance to these fundamental definitions. We shall discuss the question of groups, signals, and fronts in the following chapters, where we will also discover a fourth velocity, defining the average speed of energy transfer. A detailed comparison of these four different velocities will follow.

These problems were of theoretical importance at that time. Sommerfeld gave a general account of the question in his lectures on optics[15] which he also quoted in his lectures on electrodynamics. From these academic discussions, a number of practical applications of great importance progressively emerged during the last twenty years. Reflections and echos of radio waves on the Heaviside layers in the upper atmosphere were among the first actual problems to be discussed, then came radar signals, sonar, sounding by ultrasonics, wave-guides, and a variety of devices for guiding planes or ships. Aside from these technical applications, we have the most important problem of wave mechanics, with the Schrödinger identification of group velocity (in the wave description) with particle velocity (in the visualization by particles). Altogether, wave propagation is one of the most important chapters in theoretical physics, one which is encountered over and over again, even in nuclear energy.

Some of the old papers on the subject seem to have been ignored by many young physicists and radio engineers, who frequently spend too much time rediscovering some of the classical results. Let this book be helpful to them.

---

[15] A. Sommerfeld, reference 13, pp. 114–123; "Electrodynamics," p. 231. Academic Press. New York, 1952.

CHAPTER II

ABOUT THE PROPAGATION OF LIGHT IN DISPERSIVE MEDIA*

by

A. SOMMERFELD

1. Introduction and Results

The following investigation whose results have already been reported on at the Dresden Scientific Conference[1] is a shortened version of a paper appearing in the Festschrift on the 70th birthday of Heinrich Weber.[2] The reason for rewriting it is given by the following work of Dr. L. Brillouin, who has successfully extended the methods of complex integration used here.

Since the title refers to the propagation of "light," it must be stated that we will not deal with *natural* (polarized or unpolarized) light, i.e., light which can be obtained from real light waves with the aid of real polarizers or frequency analyzers. Such light always contains many wavelengths, and only the average wavelength can be controlled. Instead, we set up, as our incoming light signal, a well-defined special waveform consisting of a regular series of similar sine waves. If this signal were unterminated on either end, one could not even define a velocity of propagation. Since the only char-

---

* This Chapter is an authorized translation of A. Sommerfeld, *Ann. Physik* [4] **44**, 177 (1914).

[1] Under the title: Ein Einwand gegen die Relativtheorie der Elektrodynamik und seine Beseitigung [A. Sommerfeld, *Physik. Z.* **8**, 841 (1907).

[2] A. Sommerfeld, *in* "Festschrift zum 70. Geburtstage von Heinrich Weber." Teubner, Leipzig, 1912.

acteristic of an unterminated sine wave is its phase, then we could assign only the phase of the incoming light at a certain depth of the medium of propagation. We thus come to the concept of the *phase velocity*, which is the relevant quantity for all questions of interference, in other words, for the majority of optical phenomena. What is usually understood as the velocity of light (in a material medium), i.e., the velocity of light in vacuum, c, divided by the index of refraction μ, is just this phase velocity. Only in an optically empty medium (vacuum, air) is the phase velocity the same as the velocity of propagation. In a different medium, the phase velocity tells you only how the phase of the light is delayed by interaction with the medium (according to the present theory of dispersion, due to the forced oscillations of the ions or electrons in the medium) but teaches you nothing about the process of propagation; the light excitation at every point in the medium is already present forever, for an infinitely long sine wave.

In order to be able to say something about the propagation, we must, instead, have a limited wave motion: nothing until a certain moment in time, then, for instance, a series of regular sine waves, which stop after a certain time or which continue indefinitely. Such a wave motion will be called a *signal*. Here, one can speak of a propagation of the front of the wave (wavefront velocity) or also, when the wave motion is terminated, we can speak in a certain sense, of a velocity with which the end of the signal travels through the medium. The end of the signal is naturally not as distinct as the wave front which divides a region of complete rest from a region of motion. Instead, the end of the signal is followed by a long (actually, infinitely long) tail of decaying oscillations. Nevertheless, the end of the signal can be distinguished in the formulas, even if it is not too clear from the point of view of the termination of wave motion, by the condition that the forced oscillations are no longer present, and only the decaying free oscillations of the ions remain. We can always consider a terminated signal as the superposition of an earlier unterminated signal and a second unterminated signal beginning at the end of the terminated signal with opposite phase which just cancels the first signal; we thus see that the velocity of the end of the terminated signal is identical with the velocity of the wave front of an incident signal.

One must distinguish between this wavefront velocity and the *signal velocity*, i.e., that velocity *with which the main part of the wave motion propagates in the dispersive medium.* It turns out that the signal, upon propagation, does not retain its original form, that at a certain depth in the medium, very weak signals appear at first, called "forerunners," which increase to an intensity corresponding to the incident intensity. It is the essential result of Dr. Brillouin's work that the signal velocity is practically the same as the *group velocity*, whenever the incoming wavelength is different from the characteristic wavelength of the dispersive medium, i.e., when the wave motion proceeds without strong absorption.

We will show here that the wave front velocity is always identical with the velocity of light in vacuum, c, irrespective of whether the material is normally or anomalously dispersive, whether it is transparent or opaque, or whether it is simply or doubly refractive. The proof is based on the theory of dispersion of light, which explains the various optical properties of materials on the basis of the forced oscillations of the particles of the material, either electrons or ions. In the following, we call these particles ions, but include the case of pure electronic oscillations under this name. From the viewpoint of the original Maxwell theory, which considered the dielectric constant ε and consequently also the index of refraction $\sqrt{\varepsilon}$ as a characteristic constant of the material, the phase velocity $W = c/\sqrt{\varepsilon}$ would be an actual velocity of propagation with which the disturbances spread in the medium, in the same way as c is the velocity of propagation in vacuum. According to our present knowledge and our understanding of electron theory, there exists only one isotropic medium for electrodynamic phenomena, the vacuum, and the deviations from vacuum properties can be traced back to the forced oscillations of charges. When the wave front of our signal makes its way through the optical medium, it finds the particles which are capable of oscillating originally at rest,[3] (except for their thermal motion which has no effect on propagation, due to its randomness). Originally, therefore, the medium seems optically empty; only after the particles are set into

[3] This method is the result of remarks made by W. Voigt at the discussion of my paper at Dresden (reference 1).

motion, can they influence the phase and form of the light waves. The propagation of the wavefront, however, proceeds undisturbed with the velocity of light in vacuum, independently of the character of the dispersing ions.

From this remark, the subsequent conclusions of our investigation immediately become clear. Unfortunately, these conclusions are purely theoretical, and can hardly be compared with experiment, due to the smallness of the energies involved and the shortness of the periods of time available for observation. Also, we use the formulas of the dispersion theory in a somewhat more general way than can be justified physically. Namely, we extend these formulas to infinitesimally small wavelengths, while their derivation is justified only for wavelengths large compared with the distance between dispersing particles. Our conclusions state:

If we let white light fall perpendicularly on a dispersive plate, then the less refracted (and hence "faster") components of the white light do not precede the more refracted (and hence "slower") components, and the light is not red at the first instant of emergence. Instead, the wave front of each component propagates with the same velocity c through the plate, and each component contributes equally to the energy of the initially emerging light. These initially emerging forerunners do not show the colors of the components of which they are composed; instead, they have an ultraviolet wavelength determined by the dispersive power and thickness of the plate, and a very small intensity. The form of the wave motion is so greatly altered at the initial traversal of the plate while the ions are being set into motion, that there is no similarity between the form of the incident and the initially emergent light. Also, so much energy is given up in setting the ions in motion, that the initially emergent energy is very small compared with the incident energy.

We can add another closely related result of this argument: if the light signal is incident at an angle with the normal, then the signal will at first not be refracted or reflected at all. The index of refraction becomes effective only after the ions have been set into motion, while the front of the signal and the just mentioned short wavelength forerunners traverse the plate as if it were air. Further: if one has unpolarized light incident on a plate of calcite or quartz, then one does not get, at first, linear or circularly polarized light such as one could expect if the "faster" ray actually propagated faster than the "slower" ray. Moreover, here too the crystal structure is non-existent, from an optical point of view, at the beginning, and only gradually does it become effective; in the same manner, there is no double refraction at the beginning.

The original interest in our problem was connected with the theory of relativity. This theory showed that a velocity greater than that of light was impossible, whether the velocity was that of electronic or particle motions, or of the propagation of an electrodynamic or mechanical signal.[4] W. Wien remarked, however, that in the spectrum of a medium with anomalous dispersion, there can exist a region near the absorption line where the index of refraction < 1, or equivalently, where the velocity of light (whether this refers to the phase or the group velocity of light) becomes greater than c. This apparent contradiction to the theory of relativity had to be resolved.

Let n be the frequency of the light (number of waves in a time of 2π),[5] k the wave number (number of wavelengths in a distance of 2π), W the phase velocity, U the group velocity at the frequency n, and let us ignore the absorption, i.e., let k be real. Then, it is well known that

$$W = \frac{n}{k}, \qquad U = \frac{dn}{dk}$$

which can also be written

$$U = \frac{d(Wk)}{dk} = W + k\frac{dW}{dk} = W - \lambda\frac{dW}{d\lambda}$$

For anomalous dispersion, $dW/d\lambda < 0$ and thus $U > W$. Thus, if W is greater than c, then the propagation of the signal with the group velocity U will certainly lead to a velocity greater than light, which is relativistically impossible.

According to the preceding results, there is in fact no difficulty: the front of the signal propagates under all circumstances with the

---

[4] A. Einstein, *Jahrbuch der Radioaktivität* **4**, 412 (1912), Section 5; see also M. Laue, *Physik. Z.* **12**, 48 (1911).

[5] The frequency n corresponds to ω in other chapters.

velocity of light in vacuum c; the major part of the energy follows with a necessarily smaller signal velocity. This latter is, according to Dr. Brillouin, generally the same as the group velocity except near the absorption band, which is the region of anomalous dispersion. Here the group velocity loses its meaning as a signal velocity; thus the previously mentioned difficulties with the theory of relativity rest only on an overrating of the concept of group velocity compared with what is usually used as the velocity of light, the phase velocity.

We now make some general remarks about the concept of group velocity. One can, as is well known, show[6] through individual examples that for an aggregate consisting of several neighboring wavelengths, a "wave group," a maximum, or otherwise determined amplitude propagates not with velocity W but rather with U. From this, M. Laue[7] showed that for natural light which is characterized by the wavelength of its average intensity, the group velocity is the relevant quantity for the propagation of the energy into the dispersive medium. He remarks at great length that, with anomalous dispersion, due to the strong absorption which destroys the significance of a characteristic wavelength after a short path length, one can no longer sharply define the velocity of propagation of the energy. Thus, in cases where the group velocity is greater than c (or even negative — see reference 7) the principle of the equivalence of group velocity and velocity of propagation suffers an exception, since for *a statistically defined light* there does not exist a precise velocity of propagation. That the wave front must always propagate with a velocity $\leqslant c$ is deduced from general ideas about electron theory. This result agrees with our specific result. Whether the group velocity plays a role even for *individual light signals*, as we are understanding them, cannot be decided by Laue's theory. Due to the work of Dr. Brillouin however,

---

[6] See, for instance, A. Schuster, "Einführung in die theoretische Optik," Section 183. The fact that these examples do not constitute a general proof has already been stated by W. Wien, *Encykl. Math. Wiss.* **22**, No. 28 and by P. Ehrenfest, *Ann. Physik* [4] **33**, 1571 (1910). Concerning the possibility of a *negative* group velocity (A. Schuster, *loc. cit.*) near the absorption band, see the viewpoint of M. Laue mentioned below.

[7] M. Laue, *Ann. Physik* [4] **18**, 523 (1905), see especially Section **6**.

this question can be answered affirmatively, with the restriction already noted by Laue, namely, the exclusion of regions of absorption.

The present work gives the general solution of this problem by means of complex integrals in Sections 2 and 3 of this chapter. The discussion of the solution in Section 4 is based on alternative paths of integration. If the path can be deformed to the positive semi-infinite half plane of the variable of integration, then everything is at rest; this is the case for $t < x/c$ (x = depth traversed in the dispersive medium). On the other hand, for $t > x/c$, the path must be deformed toward the negative half plane, in which case it is stopped by either a pole or a branch line in the plane. The fact that the separation of the two cases occurs just when $t = x/c$ shows that the front of the signal propagates with the velocity of light in vacuum c. The residue at the pole gives an undamped excitation with the wavelength of the incident waves, and with that amplitude and phase corresponding to a regular, undistorted, propagation of this wave motion with the phase velocity W. This is the forced part of the motion. The path around the cut in the plane, on the other hand, gives a wave motion which is a function of time, depending on the characteristic frequency and damping of the ions. This part, then, describes the free oscillations of the ions set in motion by the signal. However, such a separation into forced and free oscillations is possible only for large values of $t - x/c$. The conditions for small values of $t - x/c$, i.e., for times soon after the incidence of the signal, are discussed in Section 6; the "forerunners" which occur here and cannot be separated into the above two parts, as yet, are very weak waves of short wave lengths, whose intensity and wavelength gradually increase. In Section 5 we prove the uniqueness of the solution from the conservation of energy, with special emphasis on the fact that the field is continuous at the wave front, but the gradient is not.

2. The Incident Signal

Let the dispersive medium extend from $x = 0$ where it joins the vacuum to $x = \infty$. Let the wave be incident normally, so that the optical conditions depend only on x and t; for $x = 0$ the wave will be given as a function of t. Since the reflected wave does not interest us, let this $f(t)$ correspond to the situation just behind the surface of the dispersive medium. The motion begins at $t = 0$ and is given either as Fig. 1a or by the formulas

$$f(t) = \begin{cases} 0 & (t < 0) \\ \sin \dfrac{2\pi t}{\tau} & (t > 0) \end{cases} \tag{1}$$

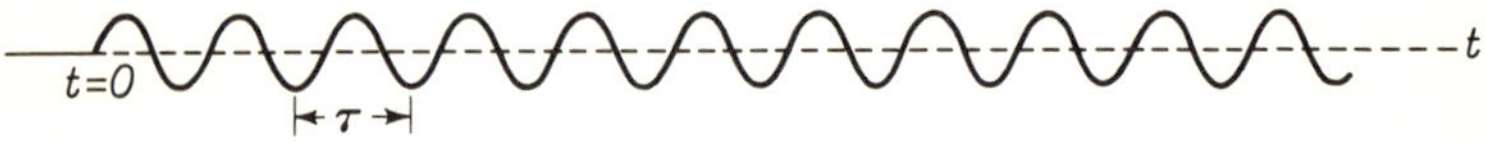

FIG. 1a.

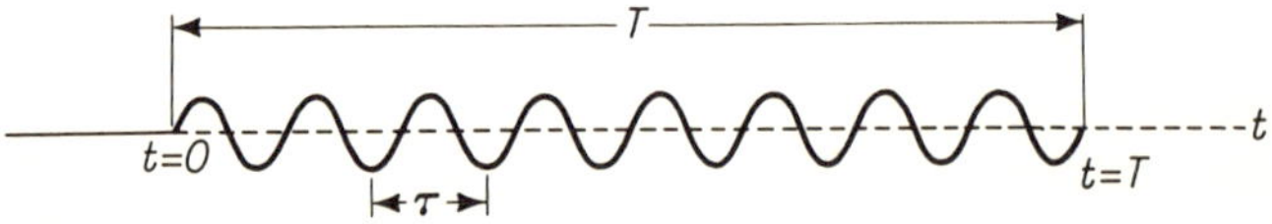

FIG. 1b.

In order to be able to use the formulas of dispersion theory, we must decompose $f(t)$ into its harmonic components of the form e^{int} (n = frequency). If one tries to do this with Fourier integrals using only real frequencies, one encounters convergence difficulties; since $f(t)$ does not vanish at $t = \infty$, the Fourier integral has no meaning. If one wants to use only the usual real form of the Fourier integral analysis, then one must consider wave forms which are terminated at both ends [$f(t) = 0$ for $t < 0$ and for $t > T$, see Fig. 1b]. Such a wave form is composed of two unterminated waves, one beginning at $t = 0$ and the second at $t = T$ with opposite phase, so that the two cancel for all time $t > T$.

For the wave terminated at both ends, one has

$$f(t) = \frac{1}{\pi} \int_0^\infty dn \int_0^T \sin 2\pi \frac{\alpha}{\tau} \cos n(t - \alpha)\, d\alpha,$$

$$= \frac{1}{2\pi} \int_0^\infty dn \left\{ \frac{\cos\left[2\pi \dfrac{\alpha}{\tau} + n(t-\alpha)\right]}{n - 2\pi/\tau} - \frac{\cos\left[2\pi \dfrac{\alpha}{\tau} - n(t-\alpha)\right]}{n + 2\pi/\tau} \right\}_{\alpha=0}^{\alpha=T}$$

In Fig. 1*b* we have set

$$T = N\tau \tag{2}$$

i.e., T is an integral multiple of τ. Then our function reduces to

$$f(t) = \frac{2}{\tau}\int_0^\infty \frac{dn}{n^2 - (2\pi/\tau)^2}\,[\cos n(t - T) - \cos nt]$$

In real from, one can rewrite this as

$$f(t) = \frac{4}{\tau}\int_0^\infty dn \sin n\left(t - \frac{T}{2}\right)\frac{\sin nT/2}{n^2 - (2\pi/\tau)^2} \tag{3}$$

In complex form, instead:

$$f(t) = \frac{1}{\tau}\int_{-\infty}^{+\infty} \frac{dn}{n^2 - (2\pi/\tau)^2}\,(e^{-in(t-T)} - e^{-int}) \tag{4}$$

or[8]

$$f(t) = \frac{1}{2\pi}\,\mathrm{Re}\int_{-\infty}^{+\infty} \frac{dn}{n - 2\pi/\tau}\,(e^{-in(t-T)} - e^{-int}) \tag{5}$$

where Re means "the real part of." Equation (3) supplies the frequency distribution of our terminated waveform in terms of infinite waves. The factor of $\sin n(t - T/2)$ is the amplitude of the individual elementary wave, its square giving the specific intensity (intensity per frequency interval).

$$J = \left(\frac{4}{\tau}\,\frac{\sin nT/2}{n^2 - (2\pi/\tau)^2}\right)^2 \tag{6}$$

One sees, therefore, that every frequency including the characteristic one of $n = 2\pi/\tau$ has a finite intensity. The vanishing of the denom-

[8] That Eqs. (4) and (5) are identical, is easily proven in the same manner by which it is shown in Section 4 that Eq. (9) is identical with Eqs. (9a, b).

inator at $n = 2\pi/\tau$ is compensated for by the vanishing of the numerator $\sin nT/2 = \sin N\pi$ [Eq. (2)]. The result of this is that

$$J_{\max} = \left(\frac{N\tau}{2\pi}\right)^2 \tag{7}$$

For Eq. (5), therefore, it follows that at $n = 2\pi/\tau$ the integrand is also not infinite as long as we do not separate the two exponentials. Thus we can replace the integration along the real axis through this point by a small semicircle in the upper half of the complex plane. Once this has been done, we can deform the path still further (see Fig. 2) and can integrate the two exponentials in Eq. (5) separately:

$$f(t) = \frac{1}{2\pi}\,\mathrm{Re}\int \frac{dn}{n - 2\pi/\tau}\, e^{-int} - \frac{1}{2\pi}\,\mathrm{Re}\int \frac{dn}{n - 2\pi/\tau}\, e^{-in(t-T)} \tag{8}$$

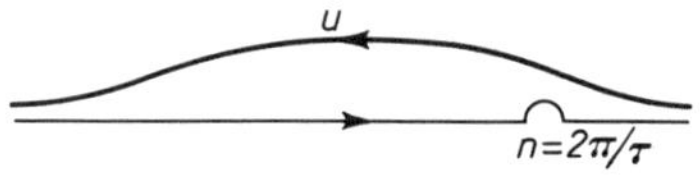

FIG. 2.

We consider u (from $+\infty$ to $-\infty$, see Fig. 2) to be the path of integration, and since this is in the opposite direction from the path of a Fourier integral, we need a change of sign in Eq. (8). In Eq. (8), we are evidently describing the signal terminated at both ends as the sum of two semi-infinite signals terminated only at one end (at $t = 0$ and at $t = T$); this description would not have been possible if we had used a real path of integration.

Before we investigate the properties of this singly terminated signal further, let us plot the "spectrum" of the signal terminated on both sides, as given in Eq. (6). The intensity vanishes, according to Eq. (6), for

$$n = \frac{2\pi}{T}, \quad \frac{4\pi}{T}, \quad \frac{6\pi}{T}, \quad \ldots$$

and is a maximum approximately halfway between these zeros. The point $n = 2\pi N/T = 2\pi/\tau$ [see Eq. (2)] is an exception, since there, instead of having zero intensity, we have the highest maximum in the spectrum, whose intensity is given by Eq. (7). Therefore, the curve of intensity (schematically shown in Fig. 3) consists of an infinite number of arcs of width $2\pi/T$ with increasing and then again decreasing height. Only in the neighborhood of $2\pi/\tau$ do the two adjacent arcs fuse into one of double width and maximum height, which [see Eq. (7)] increases with increasing N, i.e., with increasing length of the signal.

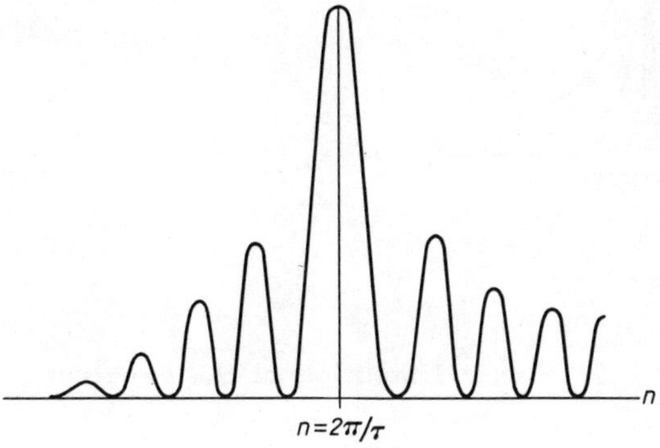

FIG. 3.

If we smooth out the intensity curve by drawing its envelope instead of each arc, and use $J/J_{\max}$ as the ordinate instead of J, then we get the schematic Fig. 4 in which the curves 1,2,3,... denote increasing values of T or correspondingly of N. Thus, the spread-out spectrum gets closer and closer to a single line of frequency $2\pi/\tau$, as was to be expected.

Naturally, the smoothed-out intensity curve no longer gives the correct time variation of our original signal. This curve represents an unterminated wave and brings out only the more or less monochromatic character of the light (depending on the length of the wave motion). On the other hand, the original spectrum in Fig. 3 is exactly equivalent to our signal. This means: if one adds together many pure harmonic and periodic waves of different frequencies, and assigns the intensity J of Fig. 3 and the phase of Eq. (3) to the wave of frequency n and adds these for the time $-\infty$ to $+\infty$, then one gets not an unterminated wave, but rather a wave which is terminated at both ends, with a characteristic frequency of $2\pi/\tau$. Evidently, it is just the large fluctuations in Fig. 3 which make it possible to reproduce the exact time variation of the signal.

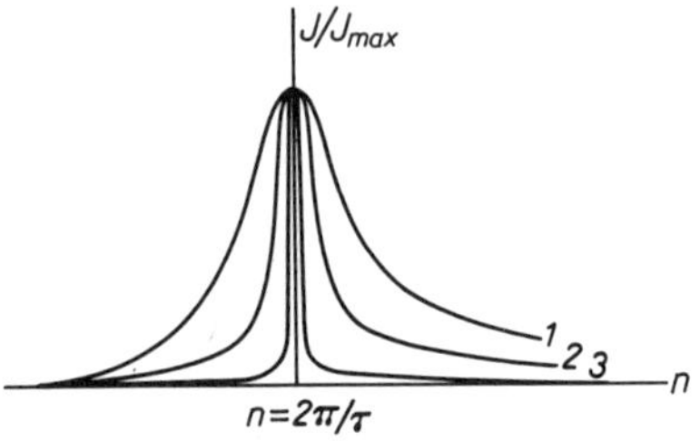

FIG. 4.

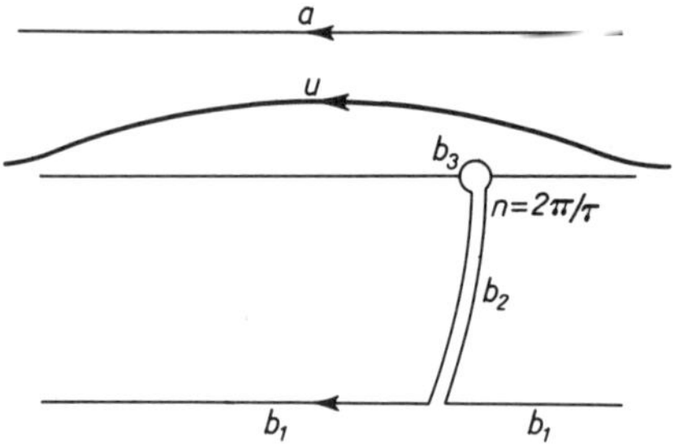

FIG. 5.

3. General Solution of the Problem

The first integral in Eq. (8) gives the signal shown in Fig. 1a, which starts at $t = 0$ and lasts until $t = \infty$; the path of integration is along u in Fig. 5.

$$f(t) = \frac{1}{2\pi} \operatorname{Re} \int e^{-int} \frac{dn}{n - 2\pi/\tau} \tag{9}$$

Although we have already shown this by Fourier analysis in the last section, let us verify this again by a method which we will need anyway for the later analysis. For this purpose, we replace the original path of integration u by two equivalent paths.

a. $t < 0$. In this case $-int$ has, in the upper half plane, a negative real part which increases indefinitely with increasing distance from the axis. One can replace the original path of integration u by the path a (Fig. 5); the integral vanishes along this path if one lets a approach infinity in the upper half plane; thus

$$f(t) = 0 \qquad (t < 0) \tag{10}$$

b. $t > 0$. Now $-int$ has a negative real part in the lower half plane, so that the exponential vanishes at infinity in this half plane.

If one tries to deform the path of integration to infinity in the lower half plane, he is held up by the singularity of the integrand at $n = 2\pi/\tau$ (Fig. 5). The path of integration b therefore consists of three parts: the part at infinity, b_1, where the integral vanishes due to the exponential factor e^{-int}; b_2, the two parts leading to infinity which cancel each other and thus contribute nothing to the integral; and the path b_3 around the singularity. This latter can immediately be evaluated by the Cauchy residue theorem:

$$b_3 = \frac{1}{2\pi} \operatorname{Re} \{2\pi i e^{-2\pi i t/\tau}\} = \sin \frac{2\pi t}{\tau} \qquad (t > 0) \tag{11}$$

Thus, it is proven that the expression (9) actually describes the type of light wave beginning at $t = 0$ defined by the conditions in Eq. (1).

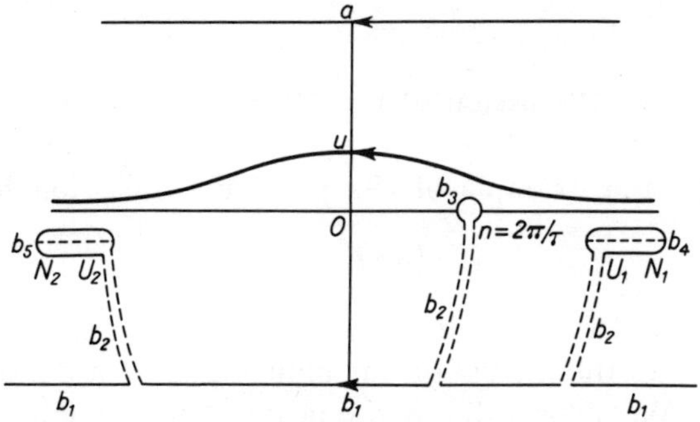

FIG. 6.

Hence, the general solution of our problem can immediately be written in the form:

$$f(t,x) = \frac{1}{2\pi} \operatorname{Re} \int e^{-int+ikx} \frac{dn}{n - 2\pi/\tau} \tag{12}$$

where the integral is taken over the path u in Fig. 5 or Fig. 6.

This is true, because the theory of dispersion shows that an unterminated wave motion at $x = 0$ of the form e^{-int} takes the form

$e^{-int+ikx}$ after moving a distance x in the dispersive medium, provided we define k by

$$k^2 = \frac{n^2}{c^2}\left(1 + \frac{a^2}{n_0^2 - 2in\rho - n^2}\right) \tag{13}$$

with the abbreviation $a^2 = \mathfrak{N}e^2/m$.

Here, $\mathfrak{N}$, e, n_0, ρ, and m represent the number per cubic centimeter, charge, characteristic frequency, damping constant, and mass of the oscillating particles, respectively. One has to consider each of these quantities as carrying a subscript if there are several kinds of oscillating particles, and sum over these subscripts. Since nothing essential is changed by doing this, we will restrict our attention to formula (13). More details on this Lorentz-Lorenz refraction formula may be found in Chapter V.

That no solution other than Eq. (12) exists will be shown in Section 5.

4. Discussion of the Obtained Solution

We follow the example of the previous discussion for $f(t)$. Let

$$\mathfrak{t} = t - x/c$$

We consider the two cases (*a*) $\mathfrak{t} < 0$ and (*b*) $\mathfrak{t} > 0$, and maintain that $\mathfrak{t} = 0$ represents the arrival of our light signal at a depth x.

a. $\mathfrak{t} < 0$. We deform the path u in Fig. 5 or Fig. 6 into the path a. This is allright, so long as the real part of $-int + ikx$ becomes negative at infinity in the upper half plane. For $n = \infty$, $k = n/c$, according to Eq. (6), and thus

$$-int + ikx = -in(t - x/c) = in\mathfrak{t}$$

Thus, the change to the path a is permitted if $\mathfrak{t} < 0$. Then the integral vanishes. Thus

$$f(t,x) = 0 \qquad t < 0 \tag{14}$$

b. $\mathfrak{t} > 0$. We deform the path u into the *lower* half plane, since $-int + ikx = -in\mathfrak{t}$ has a negative real part at infinity in this half plane. In doing this, the path becomes stuck not only at the singularity of the denominator when $n = 2\pi/\tau$, but also at the branch points of the expression for k. These latter can be found from Eq. (13), by setting $k = \infty$ and $k = 0$:

(13a) $k = \infty$, when $n^2 + 2in\rho = n_0^2$
that is, when $n = -i\rho + \sqrt{n_0^2 - \rho^2}$

(13b) $k = 0$, when $n^2 + 2in\rho = n_0^2 + a^2$
that is, when $n = -i\rho \pm \sqrt{n_0^2 + a^2 - \rho^2}$

The branch points thus lie symmetrically about the imaginary axis in the lower half plane; the first two ($k = \infty$) are called U_1, U_2 in Fig. 6, the last two ($k = 0$) are called N_1, N_2. The imaginary parts of n for all of them is $-\rho$; the real parts (for small ρ and a) do not differ much from $\pm n_0$, i.e., the characteristic frequency of the electrons. The positions of the branch points ($n_0 > 2\pi/\tau$) in Fig. 6 corresponds to an absorption in the ultraviolet, if the frequency $2\pi/\tau$ of the incident wave lies in the visible range. We join U_1 to N_1 and U_2 to N_2 by two branch lines.

The path of integration b now has the parts b_1, b_3, b_4, and b_5, since we neglected the dotted path b_2 right from the start, because its two sections always cancel. The contribution of b_1 vanishes because of the large negative real part of $-int$. The value along b_3 can again be evaluated by the residue theorem:

$$(15) \qquad b_3 = \frac{1}{2\pi} \operatorname{Re} \{2\pi i e^{-2\pi i(t/\tau) + ik_\tau x}\}$$

Here, k_τ means the value of k corresponding to $n = 2\pi/\tau$ in Eq. (13). We let

$$(16) \qquad k_\tau = \frac{2\pi}{\lambda}(1 + i\varkappa)\, e^{ik_\tau x} = e^{-2\pi\kappa x/\lambda} \cdot e^{2\pi i x/\lambda}$$

i.e., we let λ equal the distance x between waves of the same phase, and let κ equal the logarithmic decrement of the amplitude as the wave moves through one wavelength.

Then we get from Eq. (15)

$$b_3 = e^{-2\pi\kappa x/\lambda} \sin 2\pi\left(\frac{t}{\tau} - \frac{x}{\lambda}\right) \tag{17}$$

The integrals along b_4 and b_5 cannot be simplified further. We write:

$$B = b_4 + b_5 = \frac{1}{2\pi}\left(\int\right) e^{-int+ikx} \frac{dn}{n - 2\pi/\tau} \tag{18}$$

in which the parentheses about the integral sign indicate the path around both branch lines. In all, we then have

$$f(t,x) = e^{-2\pi\kappa x/\lambda} \sin 2\pi\left(\frac{t}{\tau} - \frac{x}{\lambda}\right) + B \qquad t > 0 \tag{19}$$

c. $t = 0$. In this case, we can change the original path of integration to one at infinity in either the upper or the lower half plane, since the integrand vanishes in either case, though no longer exponentially (since $e^{-int+ikx} = e^{-int} = 1$), but rather as $1/n^2$.

We can see this, for instance, in the following manner: If we take the real part in Eq. (9), we get

$$f(t) = \frac{1}{4\pi}\left(\int e^{-int} \frac{dn}{n - 2\pi/\tau} + \int e^{int} \frac{dn}{n - 2\pi/\tau}\right) \tag{9a}$$

Substitution of $+n$ for $-n$ in the second integral yields

$$f(t) = \frac{1}{\tau}\int e^{-int} \frac{dn}{n^2 - (2\pi/\tau)^2} \tag{9b}$$

Now, applying dispersion theory, we get from Eq. (9b), just as we got Eq. (12) from Eq. (9) earlier,

$$f(t,x) = \frac{1}{\tau}\int e^{-int+ikx} \frac{dn}{n^2 - (2\pi/\tau)^2} \tag{12a}$$

Here, the integrand decreases as e^{-int}/n^2 as n gets very large; thus it vanishes as $1/n^2$ for $t = 0$.

Since we can calculate $f(t,x)$ by using either path a or path b, we see that

$$(20) \qquad 0 = e^{-2\pi\kappa x/\lambda} \sin 2\pi\left(\frac{t}{\tau} - \frac{x}{\lambda}\right) + B \qquad \mathfrak{t} = 0$$

Thus, there is continuity in the transition from the region $\mathfrak{t} < 0$ to the region $\mathfrak{t} > 0$.

All together, one gets the following picture of the course of the signal at a depth x (Fig. 7):

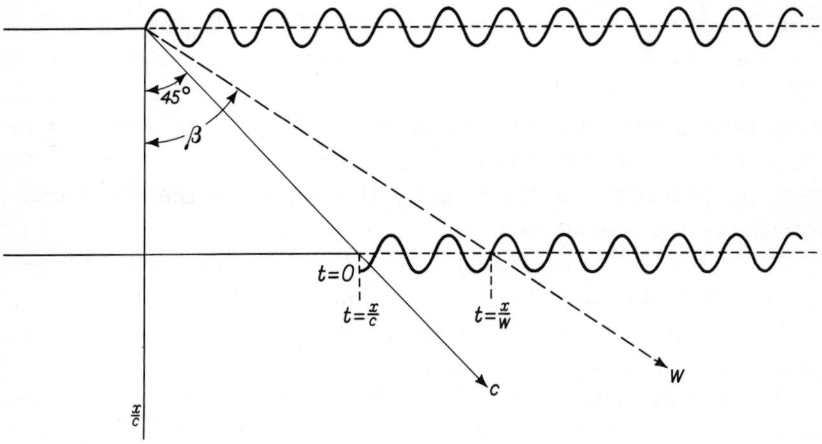

FIG. 7.

a. Until the time $t = x/c$ there is no motion. Even if the phase velocity $W > c$, no optical effect could set in earlier than one propagating with the velocity of light in vacuum c. If one uses x/c as the ordinate in Fig. 7, then the ray at 45° corresponds to a propagation with velocity c. This ray cuts the line at a depth x at the point $\mathfrak{t} = 0$ which is the time the signal begins to arrive there. If we assume normal dispersion, which means $W < c$, and draw the dotted ray at an angle β such that $ctn\beta = W/c$, then this ray denotes those points corresponding to a velocity of propagation W. Actually, however, the velocity W has nothing to do with the propagation of the light; instead, it determines the distribution of the phases, and even this, strictly speaking, only for unterminated waves.

b. The wave motion for $t > 0$ consists of two parts, which we can divide into free and forced oscillations, the first given by B [Eq. (18)], and the second [see Eq. (19)] given by

$$e^{-2\pi\kappa x/\lambda} \sin 2\pi\left(\frac{t}{\tau} - \frac{x}{\lambda}\right) = e^{-2\pi\kappa x/\lambda} \sin \frac{2\pi}{\tau}\left(t - \frac{x}{W}\right)$$

The *forced oscillation* (see Fig. 7) is undamped in time, and has the same sine wave characteristics as the incident wave; only the amplitude is diminished by the damping coefficient, though this is neglected in the figure. We construct the phase of the forced oscillations by drawing the wave as starting at $t = x/W$ (the intersection with the dotted ray) with the phase of the start of the incident wave, and this determines the phase at the time $t = x/c$. Actually, the wave motion given by Eq. (19) begins at this time ($t = 0$), and the forced motion does not actually begin at $t = x/W$. Our construction shows graphically that the velocity W determines the phase and c determines the propagation.

With anomalous dispersion ($W > c$), the dotted ray would intersect at an earlier time than $t = x/c$. The phase at the forced oscillation would be determined by this point of intersection, but the oscillation would actually begin only at time $t = x/c$.

The *free oscillations* (not shown in Fig. 7) are damped in time, since t in the expression for B is multiplied by the complex factor n, whose imaginary part equals the damping constant ρ of the oscillating ions, if one takes the path of integration for B (as one is permitted to) right at the branch points U_1N_1, U_2N_2. In any case, the free oscillations begin at the time $t = x/c$ because the ions must first be set into motion, and it takes some time for them to accommodate themselves to the incoming wave motion, on account of their inertia and their elastic forces. With increasing t this free oscillation vanishes, and only the forced oscillations (modified by the oscillations of the ions) remain.

c. For $t = 0$, the free and forced oscillations just cancel [Eq. (20)], so that the total wave motion is continuous and of zero intensity.

As was already stated in the introduction, there is no point in dividing the motion into forced and free oscillations at this time.

The actual character of the motion beginning at $t = 0$, which we will soon describe as "forerunners," has neither the period of the incoming signal nor that of the free oscillations of the ions.

Thus, most of the statements made in the introduction have been proven.

5. Uniqueness of the Solution and Boundary Conditions

Since our results are at least partly surprising, it is probably not superfluous to prove that our solution is the only possible one — that any other method of solution leads to the same result. We make use of the interesting method that was used by H. Weber[9] on the problem of the pure Maxwell theory, and we extend it to include the theory of dispersion. The uniqueness will be proven directly from the conservation of energy.

Let $\mathfrak{E} = \mathfrak{E}_y$ and $\mathfrak{H} = \mathfrak{H}_z$ be the electromagnetic field, and let $\mathfrak{s} = \mathfrak{s}_y$ be the displacements of the ions from their equilibrium positions, all of which are functions of only x and t and have nonzero values only for $x > 0$ and $t > 0$. Then the basic equations are:[10]

$$\frac{1}{c}\dot{\mathfrak{H}} = -\frac{\partial \mathfrak{E}}{\partial x}$$

$$\frac{1}{c}(\dot{\mathfrak{E}} + \mathfrak{N} e \dot{\mathfrak{s}}) = -\frac{\partial \mathfrak{H}}{\partial x} \tag{21}$$

$$m\ddot{\mathfrak{s}} + 2h\dot{\mathfrak{s}} + f\mathfrak{s} = e\mathfrak{E}$$

if one neglects the effect of the magnetic field on the ions to first order, which would contribute another term $e\dot{\mathfrak{s}}\mathfrak{H}/c$ on the right side of the last equation. Multiplying the three equations by $c\mathfrak{H}$, $c\mathfrak{E}$, and $\mathfrak{N}\dot{\mathfrak{s}}$ and adding gives

---

[9] H. Weber, "Partielle Differentialgleichungen," Vol. II, Section 167. The method actually comes from E. Cohn, "Elektromagnetisches Feld," Chapter VI, Section 5. It can easily be generalized to the case of several boundaries and a field depending on all three space coordinates. For the purposes of this paper, only one coordinate x is needed and only one boundary at $x = ct$.

[10] In the notation of Section 3, Eq. (13), $h/m = \rho$ and $f/m = n_0^2$

$$\dot{\mathfrak{H}}\mathfrak{H} + \dot{\mathfrak{E}}\mathfrak{E} + \mathfrak{N}(m\dot{\mathfrak{s}}\ddot{\mathfrak{s}} + 2h\dot{\mathfrak{s}}^2 + f\mathfrak{s}\dot{\mathfrak{s}}) = -c\left(\mathfrak{E}\frac{\partial\mathfrak{H}}{\partial x} + \mathfrak{H}\frac{\partial\mathfrak{E}}{\partial x}\right)$$

$$= -\frac{\partial\mathfrak{S}}{\partial x}$$

where $\mathfrak{S}$ denotes the energy flux. Integrating with respect to x from 0 to ∞ and with respect to t from 0 to t results in

$$\frac{1}{2}\int\left[\mathfrak{H}^2 + \mathfrak{E}^2 + \mathfrak{N}(m\dot{\mathfrak{s}}^2 + f\mathfrak{s}^2\right]_{t=0}^{t=t} dx + 2h\mathfrak{N}\int_0^t dt\int_0^\infty \dot{\mathfrak{s}}^2 dx = -\left[\int_0^t \mathfrak{S}dt\right]_{x=0}^{x=\infty}$$

(22)

Now, let $\mathfrak{E}_1,\mathfrak{H}_1,\mathfrak{s}_1$ and $\mathfrak{E}_2,\mathfrak{H}_2,\mathfrak{s}_2$ be two different solutions of these basic equations, satisfying the conditions:

(23) for $x = 0$ and all $t > 0$: $\mathfrak{E}_1 = \mathfrak{E}_2$

for $x = \infty$ and all $t > 0$: $\mathfrak{E}_1 = \mathfrak{E}_2$

for $t = 0$ and all $x > 0$: $\mathfrak{E}_1 = \mathfrak{E}_2$, $\mathfrak{H}_1 = \mathfrak{H}_2$, $\mathfrak{s}_1 = \mathfrak{s}_2$

Then $\mathfrak{E} = \mathfrak{E}_1 - \mathfrak{E}_2$, $\mathfrak{H} = \mathfrak{H}_1 - \mathfrak{H}_2$, $\mathfrak{s} = \mathfrak{s}_1 - \mathfrak{s}_2$ must also satisfy not only the basic Eqs. (21) but also Eq. (22) in which, by virtue of Eq. (23), the terms to be evaluated at $t = 0$, $x = 0$, and $x = \infty$ vanish. Then the only remaining terms are:

$$\frac{1}{2}\int(\mathfrak{E}^2 + \mathfrak{H}^2)\,dx + \frac{\mathfrak{N}}{2}\int(m\dot{\mathfrak{s}}^2 + f\mathfrak{s}^2)\,dx + 2h\mathfrak{N}\int_0^t dt\int_0^\infty \dot{\mathfrak{s}}^2\,dx = 0 \tag{24}$$

where the first two integrals refer to the time t. From this we may infer that

$$\mathfrak{H} = \mathfrak{E} = \mathfrak{s} = 0$$

since each term on the left side can never be negative. The above three terms refer to magnetic and electric energy of the field, kinetic and potential energy of the ions, and the energy lost by the damping of the ionic motions, respectively.

If we had several types of ions instead of just one, then Eq. (24) would consist of the sums of their energies and their energy losses, and the conclusion would not be altered. Even more important for us is the fact that our result will still be valid if the domain of integration $0 < x < \infty$ is broken up into several parts $0 < x < x_1$, $x_1 < x < x_2, \ldots$, in each of which the basic equations are satisfied, *so long as* $\mathfrak{E}$ *and* $\mathfrak{H}$ *and also* $\mathfrak{s}$ *and* $\dot{\mathfrak{s}}$ *are continuous at the boundaries,* which can change with t. Their derivatives, however, can be discontinuous. Then, since one integrates over x in parts, from 0 to x_1, x_1 to $x_2 \ldots$, one has to replace $[\mathfrak{S}]_0^\infty$ with $[\mathfrak{S}]_0^{x_1} + [\mathfrak{S}]_{x_1}^{x_2} + \ldots$ which becomes $[\mathfrak{S}]_0^\infty$ because of the postulated continuity of $\mathfrak{E}$ and $\mathfrak{H}$. Similarly, one has to integrate in parts over t on the left side of Eq. (22), from 0 to t_1, t_1 to t_2, where $t_1, t_2 \ldots$ are the times at which the boundaries pass the just-mentioned points. Because of the postulated continuity of $\mathfrak{E}, \mathfrak{H}, \mathfrak{s}$, and $\dot{\mathfrak{s}}$, none of these points contribute to Eq. (22). Thus, the uniqueness is proven in this case also.

The use of these results in the problem discussed in the previous paragraphs is as follows: when $t = 0$, there is no motion in the whole dispersive medium:

$$\mathfrak{E} = \mathfrak{H} = \mathfrak{s} = 0 \qquad \text{for } t = 0 \text{ and } x > 0 \tag{25}$$

The thermal motions of the ions are here neglected; their contributions can be made negligibly small by increasing the intensity of the signal or by decreasing the temperature. For $x = \infty$, which is reached by the signal only after an infinite time, there is likewise no motion at any time; thus it is true, in particular, that

$$\mathfrak{E} = 0 \qquad \text{for } x = \infty \text{ and } t > 0 \tag{25a}$$

For $x = 0$, $\mathfrak{E}$ is given.

$$\mathfrak{E} = f(t) \qquad \text{for } x = 0 \text{ and } t > 0 \tag{25b}$$

These conditions (25) are just those required earlier in conditions (23).

As boundaries, we have to consider the plane $x = ct$. At these boundaries, $\mathfrak{E}$ is continuous. It was shown earlier (cf. the previous paragraphs under *c.*) that $\mathfrak{E} = 0$ whether one approaches the boundary from $x < ct$ or from $x > ct$. One can prove similarly, that $\mathfrak{H}$, $\mathfrak{s}$, and $\dot{\mathfrak{s}}$ are also continuous. Namely, if $\mathfrak{E}$ is given by Eq. (12a)

$$\mathfrak{E} = \int e^{-int+ikx}\,\phi(n)dn$$

where

$$\phi(n) = \frac{1}{\tau}\,\frac{1}{n^2-(2\pi/\tau)^2}$$

then the corresponding $\mathfrak{H}$ and $\mathfrak{s}$ are given by the first and third basic equation as

$$\mathfrak{H} = \int \frac{kc}{n}\,e^{-int+ikx}\,\phi(n)\,dn$$

$$\mathfrak{s} = e\int e^{-int+ikx}\,\frac{\phi(n)\,dn}{-m\,n^2-2hin+f}$$

One can directly apply the same analysis used under c in the preceding paragraphs to these integrals. Thus, just as $\mathfrak{E}$ vanishes as one approaches the boundary $x = ct$ from either side, so also do $\mathfrak{H}$, $\mathfrak{s}$, and $\dot{\mathfrak{s}}$. With this, as well as the conditions (25), we have proven the uniqueness of our solution and shown that no other solution exists.

Concerning the validity of dispersion theory, we wish to mention one restriction which underlies all calculations of dispersion: that there must be very many particles within a wavelength. Only under this condition can we reckon on a continuous distribution of displacement vectors $\mathfrak{s}$ and disregard the molecular discontinuities. This condition is, as is well known, satisfied for wavelengths as short as ultraviolet, but not for very high (x-ray) frequencies. In so far as we must include these frequencies in our analytical method, we are applying an extrapolation of the formulas of dispersion theory in a realm where their validity is not physically justified.

I want to include another interesting remark, for which I am indebted to a letter from Dr. T. Levi-Civita. He brought my attention to the fact that one can prove that the propagation of the wave front proceeds with the velocity of light in vacuum c directly from the basic relations (21), due to the so-called "compatibility relations."[11]

[11] More about this can be found, for example, in G. Zemplen, *Encykl. Math. Wiss.* 4, Art. 19.

Let

$$e = \left[\frac{\partial \mathfrak{E}}{\partial x}\right] \qquad h = \left[\frac{\partial \mathfrak{H}}{\partial x}\right] \tag{26}$$

be the discontinuities in $(\partial\mathfrak{E}/\partial x)$, $(\partial\mathfrak{H}/\partial x)$ at the boundary (the wave front). Since $\mathfrak{E}$, $\mathfrak{H}$, and $\dot{\mathfrak{s}}$ prove to be continuous we have:

$$[\mathfrak{E}] = [\mathfrak{H}] = [\dot{\mathfrak{s}}] = 0 \tag{26a}$$

If v represents the velocity with which the discontinuity moves in the direction of its normal, then the "identity compatibility relations" state that:

$$[\dot{\mathfrak{E}}] = -ve \qquad [\dot{\mathfrak{H}}] = -vh \tag{26b}$$

This follows directly, if one writes the equation

$$\mathfrak{E}(t + \Delta t,\, x + \Delta x) - \mathfrak{E}(t,x) = \dot{\mathfrak{E}}\Delta t + \frac{\partial \mathfrak{E}}{\partial x}\Delta x$$

for the two sides of the boundary, subtracts them, and sets $\Delta x = v\Delta t$. Proceeding similarly with the basic Eqs. (21), and using Eqs. (26), (26a), and (26b), we get:

$$-\frac{v}{c}h = -e \qquad -\frac{v}{c}e = -h$$

so that upon multiplying the two,

$$\frac{v^2}{c^2} = 1 \tag{27}$$

which is our result: the velocity of the wave front is the velocity of light in vacuum.

6. The Forerunners

We can handle the situation arising immediately after the start of the signal, i.e., for small values of $\mathfrak{t} = t - x/c$, in the following manner.

We start with Eq. (12a) of Section 4 which is to be evaluated along the original path u. This is

$$f(t,x) = \frac{1}{\tau}\int e^{-int+iKx}\frac{dn}{n^2-(2\pi/\tau)^2} \tag{28}$$

with the abbreviation

$$K = k - \frac{n}{c} = \frac{n}{c}\left\{\sqrt{1+\frac{a^2}{n_0{}^2-n^2}}-1\right\} \tag{28a}$$

Here and in the ensuing we neglect the damping of the ionic oscillations, i.e., we set $\rho = 0$ which also makes the coefficient of absorption $\kappa = 0$.

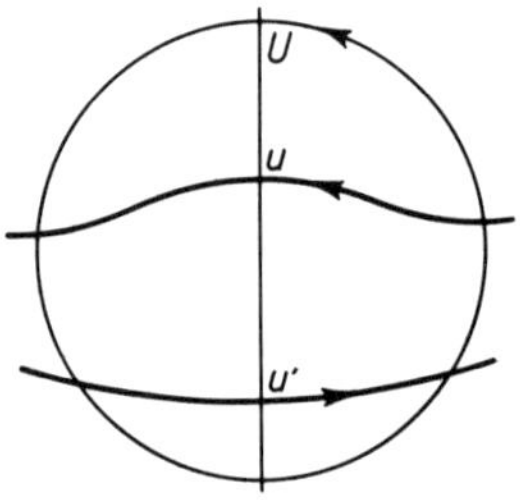

FIG. 8.

We add another path of integration u' in the lower half plane to the path u (Fig. 8); this is permissible since, for $t > 0$, we can deform the path u' to one at infinity in the lower half plane just as we did with path b_1 in Figs. 5 and 6. The two paths u and u' can be combined to a path U far from the origin of the n plane, upon which the integration in Eq. (28) is to be performed.

Since n is very large along the whole path U, we expand the square root in K and retain only the lowest power of $1/n$.

We then get

$$Kx = \frac{a^2x}{2c}\frac{n}{n_0{}^2-n^2}\left(1-\frac{1}{4}\frac{a^2}{n_0{}^2-n^2}+\ldots\right) = -\frac{\xi}{n}$$

with the notation

$$\xi = \frac{a^2x}{2c} \tag{29}$$

Our integral (28) now reads, if we replace the denominator $n^2 - (2\pi/\tau)^2$ by n^2,

$$f(t,x) = \frac{1}{\tau} \int e^{-int - i\frac{\xi}{n}} \frac{dn}{n^2} \tag{30}$$

We can write the above exponential in the following manner:

$$-i\left(n\mathrm{t} + \frac{\xi}{n}\right) = -i\sqrt{\mathrm{t}\xi}\left(n\sqrt{\frac{\mathrm{t}}{\xi}} + \frac{1}{n}\sqrt{\frac{\xi}{\mathrm{t}}}\right) = -2i\sqrt{\mathrm{t}\xi}\cos u$$

where the new variable of integration u is defined by

$$e^{in} = n\sqrt{\frac{\mathrm{t}}{\xi}} \tag{31}$$

where by

$$\frac{dn}{n^2} = idu\sqrt{\frac{\mathrm{t}}{\xi}}\, e^{-iu}$$

Thus, Eq. (30) is rewritten as

$$f(t,x) = \frac{1}{\tau}\sqrt{\frac{\mathrm{t}}{\xi}} \int e^{-2i\sqrt{\mathrm{t}\xi}\cos u}\, e^{-iu}\, idu \tag{32}$$

Here we let the variable u vary from 0 to 2π. According to Eq. (31), this corresponds to a circuit about the origin of the n-plane in a circle of radius $|n| = \sqrt{\xi/\mathrm{t}}$, i.e., for very small t a path U, as was required in Fig. 8. The integral appearing in Eq. (32) is nothing but a well-known integral representation of the Bessel function[12] of the first order of argument $2\sqrt{\mathrm{t}\xi}$ and we thus have

$$f(t,x) = \frac{2\pi}{\tau}\sqrt{\frac{\mathrm{t}}{\xi}}\, J_1(2\sqrt{\mathrm{t}\xi}) \tag{33}$$

From the well-known character of the function J_1, we find the following as the condition of our signal right after it arrives, i.e., for

[12] E. Jahnke and F. Emde, "Funktionentafeln, 4th" ed., p. 149. Dover, New York, 1945.

small values of $\mathfrak{t}$. The initial amplitude is negligibly small compared with 1, i.e., compared with the amplitude of the incoming wave, and the initial period of the wave is small compared with τ, i.e., compared with the incident period. Period and amplitude increase because of the occurrence of $\sqrt{\mathfrak{t}}$ before and in the function J_1, respectively, as is schematically shown in Fig. 9, where one must remember that our last Eq. (32), from the manner in which it was derived, is valid only for small values of $\mathfrak{t}/\xi$. The situation for large values of $\mathfrak{t}$ and the way the forerunners join on to the main signal of period τ, are taken up by Dr. Brillouin in the following chapters.

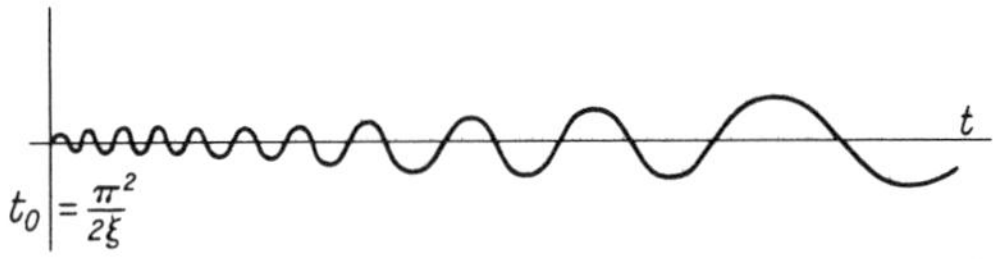

FIG. 9.

One point of exceptional interest should still be made.

According to Eq. (32), the period of the initial forerunner is given by the first root of the function $J_1(z)$ which is approximately $z = \pi$. From this, one calculates the initial period $\mathfrak{t}_0$ using Eq. (29) as

$$\mathfrak{t}_0 = \frac{\pi^2}{2\xi} = \frac{\pi^2 c}{a^2 x}$$

This time is independent of the period τ of the incident light, as well as of the characteristic frequency of the oscillating ions, and is determined only by the depth x and the dispersive capability of the medium, i.e., by the number of ions $\mathfrak{N}$. This independence of the period from the color of the incident light was already used in some inferences in the introduction.

CHAPTER III

ABOUT THE PROPAGATION OF LIGHT IN DISPERSIVE MEDIA*

1. How to Use the Saddle-Point Method of Integration

In the present chapter, we discuss the problem which Dr. Sommerfeld proposed in the preceding chapter. The propagation of a signal terminated on one side, which is what is involved here, leads to the integral

$$f(t,x) = \frac{1}{2\pi} \operatorname{Re} \int \frac{e^{-i(nt - kx)}}{n - \nu} dn \tag{1}$$

which is to be evaluated in the complex plane n from $+\infty$ to $-\infty$ over the path u [compare with Section 2, Fig. 2 and Eq. (9) of Chapter II]. $\nu = 2\pi/\tau$ is the frequency, τ the period of the signal, k has the value

$$k = \frac{n}{c}\mu \tag{2}$$

where c is the velocity of light in vacuum, and μ denotes the complex index of refraction for the frequency n. [Compare Chapter II, formula (13).]

$$\mu^2 = 1 + \frac{a^2}{{n_0}^2 - 2in\rho - n^2} \tag{2'}$$

The integral (1) gives the signal at time t and a depth x of the medium with index of refraction μ. The exponent of e is denoted by w.

---

* L. Brillouin, *Ann. Physik* [4] 44, 203 (1914).

$$w = -i(nt - kx) = \frac{x}{c} v \tag{3}$$

$$v = -in(\Theta - \mu) \tag{4}$$

$$\Theta = \frac{ct}{x} \tag{4a}$$

A signal propagating with velocity c would arrive at a depth x at a time $t = x/c$, that is, for $\Theta = 1$. In Chapter II, Sommerfeld showed that a signal never propagates with a velocity greater than that of light, i.e. that $f(t,x)$ vanishes for $\Theta < 1$. Let us denote

$$\Theta - 1 = \mathfrak{d} \tag{4b}$$

$$t - \frac{x}{c} = \mathfrak{t} \tag{4c}$$

This chapter will examine the form of the signal and show that one can give an exact definition of the concept of the signal velocity and that this velocity is identical with the group velocity, except for signals whose wavelengths are in the region of the anomalous dispersion of the medium.

Let ξ, η be the coordinates of the complex plane n:

$$n = \xi + i\eta$$

and let X, Y be the real and imaginary parts of the function v

$$v = X + iY$$

For a discussion of the integral, it is simplest to deform the path of integration in such a way that X, in general, takes on large negative values; then the integral vanishes, and one has to evaluate the integral only for those parts of the path for which the absolute value of X is not too large.

It is well known that, due to the equations

$$\frac{\partial X}{\partial \xi} = \frac{\partial Y}{\partial \eta} \qquad \frac{\partial X}{\partial \eta} = -\frac{\partial Y}{\partial \xi}$$

the function X has no maximum or minimum of finite value; there can be only saddle points, where

$$\frac{\partial X}{\partial \xi} = \frac{\partial X}{\partial \eta} = 0$$

At such a point, Y also has a saddle point; the point is determined by the equation

$$\frac{dv}{dn} = 0 \tag{5}$$

In the following, the complex plane will be regarded as a topographical map with X as the elevation, and the equipotential lines and lines of steepest descent of X will be considered. The lines of descent for X are equipotential lines for Y. They can originate only from those points at which X is infinite, since no finite maxima or minima occur. The transition from one valley to another proceeds most easily across a saddle point. The integration in the neighborhood of the saddle point will be of greatest interest.[1] It will turn out that those saddle points which are of interest always lie near the real axis.

According to Eq. (5), the condition for a saddle point, taking Eq. (3) into account, is:

$$t - \frac{dk}{dn} x = 0 \tag{6}$$

If n is real, i.e., if it corresponds to an actual frequency, then the group velocity of this frequency (compare with Chapter II, Section 1) is equal to dn/dk. Consequently, at time t the saddle point is at that frequency n whose group velocity is x/t. In the evaluation of the integral, one can restrict one's attention to the neighborhood of the saddle point, i.e., to the neighborhood of this frequency. Therefore, it is approximately true that every elementary wave motion of the signal spreads with its group velocity, at least so long as its domain remains normally dispersive.

---

[1] For a discussion of the method of saddle points and its use see P. Debye, *Math. Ann.* **67**, 535 (1910); *Sitzber. bayer. Akad. Wiss. Math.-naturw. Kl.* (1910); first used by G. F. B. Riemann, "Gesammelte Werke," p. 400. Leipzig, 1876.

Survey

In Section 2, the complex n plane will be examined, especially near the points where X becomes zero or infinite. Section 3 gives the position of the various saddle points, their motion as a function of time, and a little about the order of magnitude of the quantities entering the formulas. In Section 4, the variation of the path of integration with time is recorded. From this, several general statements about the signal velocity follow. Section 5 contains the integration in the neighborhood of the saddle points, i.e., the calculation of the forerunners. These results enable one to calculate, in Section 6, the signal velocity also for the case of anomalous dispersion. The conclusion contains a few remarks about the comparison between the method used here, "the method of saddle points," and the so-called "method of stationary phase."

2. Examination of the Complex n Plane

It is important to know the areas of the complex n plane, in which the real part X of the exponent is negative. The border of this area is given by the equation $X = 0$. It is known how X behaves at infinity (see Chapter II, Section 4):

for $\Theta < 1$, X is at infinity: $-\infty$ in the upper half plane, and $+\infty$ in the lower half plane.

for $\Theta = 1$, X vanishes at infinity.

for $\Theta > 1$, X is at infinity: $+\infty$ in the upper half plane, and $-\infty$ in the lower half plane.

Besides this, *on the real axis* [see Chapter II, formula (16)],

$$k = \frac{2\pi}{\lambda}(1 + i\kappa) \tag{7}$$

(λ = wavelength in the dispersive medium, κ = coefficient of absorption.) One can rewrite Eq. (2) as

$$k = \frac{n}{c}\mu_r(1 + i\kappa)$$

if the complex index of refraction is given by

$$\mu = \mu_r + i\mu_i \qquad \mu_i = \kappa\mu_r \tag{7'}$$

As is well known, c/μ_r gives the phase velocity W. Now, according to Eq. (4), the real part of $v = -in(\Theta - \mu)$ is

$$X = -n\mu_i = -n\kappa\mu_r$$

Thus, X is negative along the real axis except for those frequencies n at which the coefficient of absorption vanishes. The absolute value of X is large for the regions of anomalous dispersion, small for very small or very large n.

Now consider X along the straight lines $\eta = -\rho$, determined by the points N_1, N_2 (where X vanishes) and U_1, U_2 (where X becomes infinite) and in the neighborhood of the branch lines N_1U_1 and N_2U_2. The coordinates of these points are (Chapter II, Section 4):

$$U_1, U_2 \qquad \eta = -\rho \qquad \xi_\infty = \pm\sqrt{n_0^2 - \rho^2}$$

$$N_1, N_2 \qquad \eta = -\rho \qquad \xi_n = \pm\sqrt{n_0^2 + a^2 - \rho^2}$$

Along the straight lines $\eta = -\rho$, μ has the value

$$\mu = \sqrt{1 + \frac{a^2}{\xi_\infty^2 - \xi^2}} \tag{8}$$

i.e., μ is real and positive in the regions $0 < \xi < \xi_\infty$, $\xi_n < \xi < \infty$, pure imaginary for $\xi_\infty < \xi < \xi_n$, and actually positive on one side of the cut $\xi_n\xi_\infty$, negative on the other side. In order to determine these signs, consider μ in the neighborhood of the points U_1, N_1.

For the region about N_1,

$$n = -i\rho + \xi_n + re^{i\alpha}$$

where r, α are polar coordinates about the point N_1; from this,

$$\begin{aligned} \mu^2 &= \frac{2\xi_n}{a^2} re^{i\alpha} \\ \mu &= \frac{\sqrt{2\xi_n r}}{a} e^{i\alpha/2} \end{aligned} \tag{9}$$

Therefore, for

$$\alpha = 0 \qquad \mu_0 = \frac{\sqrt{2\xi_n r}}{a},$$

$$\alpha = \frac{\pi}{2} \qquad \mu_{\pi/2} = \mu_0 \frac{1+i}{\sqrt{2}},$$

$$\alpha = \pi \qquad \mu_\pi = +\mu_0 i,$$

$$\alpha = -\frac{\pi}{2} \qquad \mu_{-\pi/2} = \mu_0 \frac{1-i}{\sqrt{2}},$$

$$\alpha = -\pi \qquad \mu_{-\pi} = -\mu_0 i$$

Similarly, in the region about U_1 let

$$n = -i\rho + \xi_\infty + Re^{i\omega}$$

and then

$$\mu^2 = -\frac{a^2}{2\xi_\infty R} e^{-i\omega} = \frac{a^2}{2\xi_\infty R} e^{+i(\pi-\omega)}$$

(10)

$$\mu = \frac{a}{\sqrt{2\xi_\infty R}} e^{i(\pi-\omega)/2}$$

Thus for

$$\omega = \pi \qquad \mu_\pi = +\infty,$$

$$\omega = \frac{\pi}{2} \qquad \mu_{\pi/2} = (1+i)\infty$$

$$\omega = 0 \qquad \mu_0 = +i\infty$$

$$\omega = \frac{3\pi}{2} \qquad \mu_{3\pi/2} = (1-i)\infty$$

$$\omega = 2\pi \qquad \mu_{2\pi} = -i\infty$$

This is shown in the adjoining Fig. 1. Thus, one can easily see, that X [$=$ real part of $v = -in(\Theta - \mu)$] is negative on both sides of the cut near N_1. This is because $\Theta \geqslant 1$ (see Section 1). Near U_1, however, X is negative on the upper side of the cut and positive on the other.

Formula (8) gives the value of μ on the straight lines $\eta = -\rho$. The value of X is derived from this:

$$X = -\rho(\Theta - \mu_r), \qquad \text{if } \mu \text{ is real,}$$

$$X = -(\rho\Theta \pm \xi\mu_i), \qquad \text{if } \mu \text{ is pure imaginary.}$$

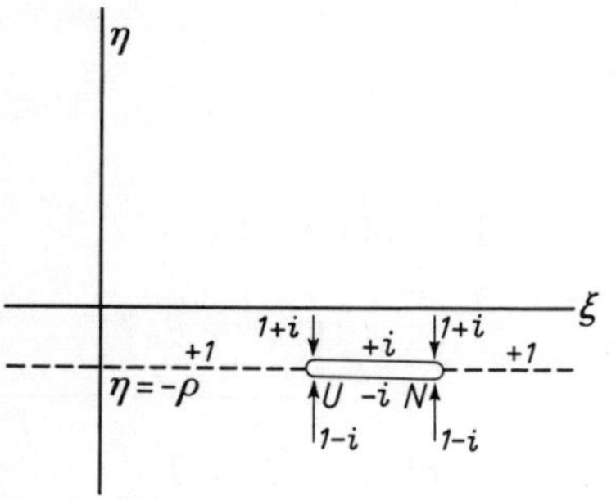

FIG. 1.

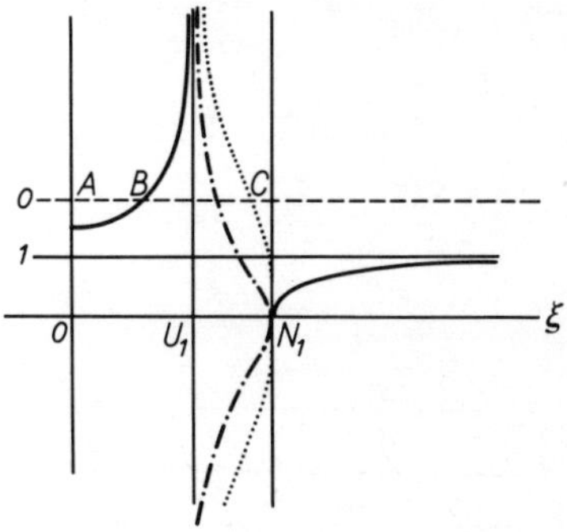

FIG. 2. Key: ———, μ_r; —·—·—, $\pm\,\mu_i$; · · · ·, $\pm\,(\xi/\rho)\mu_i$

In Fig. 2, μ_r, $\pm\,\mu_i$, and $\pm\,(\xi/\rho)\mu_i$ are plotted as ordinates, taking ξ as the abscissa (along the straight line $\eta = -\rho$). The points $X = 0$ are then given by the intersections of μ_r or of $\pm\,(\xi/\rho)\mu_i$ with a line parallel to the ξ-axis at the value Θ. For $\Theta \geqslant 1$, one of these points lies between N_1 and U_1 and actually at the bottom side of the cut. Its abscissa is $\xi = AC$. With increasing Θ, it moves from N_1 toward U_1. A second intersection with an abscissa of $\xi = AB$ can occur between 0 and U_1.

From the behavior of X near U_1, it is seen that the curve $X = 0$ must start at this point U_1. For the neighborhood of U_1

$$\mu = \frac{a}{\sqrt{2\xi_\infty R}}\left(\sin\frac{\omega}{2} + i\cos\frac{\omega}{2}\right)$$

so that

$$X = -\rho\Theta + \frac{a}{\sqrt{2\xi_\infty R}}\left(\rho \sin\frac{\omega}{2} - \xi_\infty \cos\frac{\omega}{2}\right)$$

Let ω_1 be a solution of the equation

$$\tan\frac{\omega_1}{2} = \frac{\xi_\infty}{\rho}$$

Then, assuming $\xi_\infty \gg \rho$, ω_1 is an angle near π defined modulo 2π. Then,

$$X = -\rho\Theta + \frac{b}{\sqrt{R}}\sin\frac{\omega - \omega_1}{2}$$

with the abbreviation

$$b = a\sqrt{\frac{\rho^2 + \xi_\infty{}^2}{2\xi_\infty}}$$

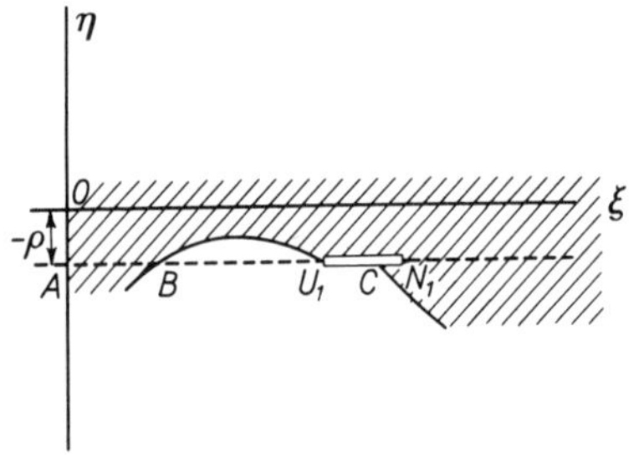

FIG. 3.

The curve $X = 0$ is then, for small R and small $(\omega - \omega_1)$, the spiral

$$\omega = \omega_1 + \frac{2\rho\Theta}{b}\sqrt{R}$$

which touches the straight line $\omega = \omega_1$ at U_1.

The adjoining Fig. 3 shows a picture of the complex plane near the cut U_1N_1. In the shaded regions, X is negative.

3. Location of the Saddle Points

What is of most interest is not so much the curve $X = 0$ as the location of the saddle points. Once these are found, then the path of integration will be taken along the lines of steepest descent through the saddle points without any difficulty. The curve $X = 0$ is one of the equipotentials orthogonal to these lines of steepest descent.

A. The region about the origin

In order to find the saddle points near the origin μ is expanded in increasing powers of n:

$$\mu = \sqrt{1 + \frac{a^2}{n_0^2 - 2i\rho n - n^2}} = \sqrt{\frac{n_2^2 - 2i\rho n - n^2}{n_0^2 - 2i\rho n - n^2}}$$

where

$$n_2^2 = n_0^2 + a^2$$

Then $(n_2^2 - \alpha)/(n_0^2 - \alpha)$ must be expanded, with $\alpha = 2i\rho n + n^2$ small compared with n_0^2 and with n_2^2:

$$\frac{n_2^2 - \alpha}{n_0^2 - \alpha} = \frac{n_2^2}{n_0^2}\left(1 - \frac{\alpha}{n_2^2}\right)\left(1 + \frac{\alpha}{n_0^2} + \ldots\right)$$

$$\mu = \frac{n_2}{n_0}\left(1 + \frac{\alpha}{2}\frac{a^2}{n_0^2 n_2^2} + \ldots\right)$$

If α is inserted and A is defined as

$$A = \frac{a^2}{2n_0^3 n_2}$$

one gets

$$\mu = \frac{n_2}{n_0} + An(n + 2i\rho) + \ldots \tag{11}$$

Thus, according to Eq. (4)

$$v = -in(\Theta - \mu) = -in[\mathfrak{d}' - An(n + 2i\rho)] \tag{12}$$

if (see Eq. 4b)

$$\mathfrak{d}' = \Theta - \frac{n_2}{n_0} = \mathfrak{d} - \left(\frac{n_2}{n_0} - 1\right) \tag{12'}$$

In order to get the saddle points, one must write

$$\frac{dv}{dn} = 0 \qquad \text{and} \qquad \mathfrak{d}' - An(3n + 4i\rho) = 0$$

The roots of this equation are

$$n = -\frac{2}{3} i\rho \pm \frac{1}{3}\sqrt{\frac{3\mathfrak{d}'}{A} - 4\rho^2}$$

Case A 1: $\mathfrak{d}' < \frac{4}{3} A\rho^2$.

The saddle points are given by

$$n = i\left(-\frac{2}{3}\rho \pm \frac{1}{3}\sqrt{4\rho^2 - \frac{3\mathfrak{d}'}{A}}\right) \tag{13}$$

They lie on the imaginary axis and are symmetric about the point $\xi = 0$, $\eta = -\frac{2}{3}\rho$. One can easily show that the lines of steepest descent through these points are parallel to the axes (see Fig. 4). The arrows show the directions of ascent along the lines of descent.

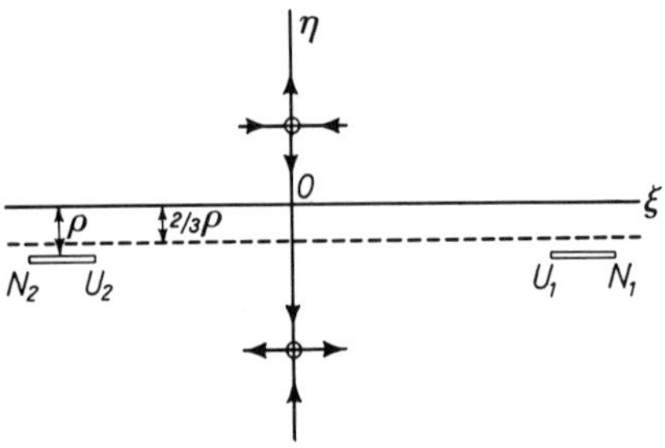

FIG. 4.

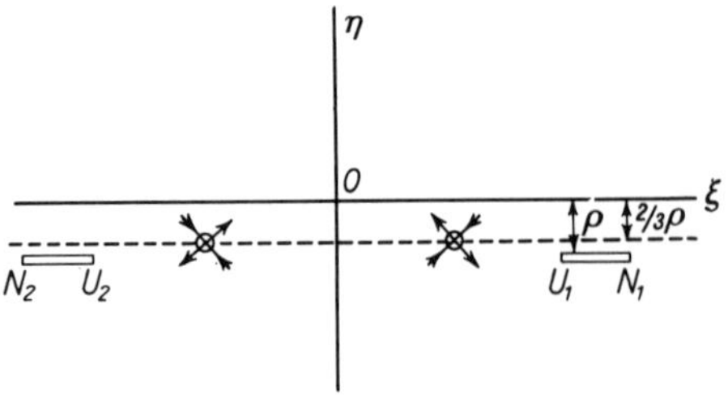

FIG. 5.

Case A 2: $\mathfrak{d}' > \frac{4}{3} A\rho^2$.

The saddle points lie on the straight line $\eta = \frac{2}{3}\rho$ symmetrically about the imaginary axis:

$$n = -i\frac{2}{3}\rho \pm \xi_p$$

(14)

$$\xi_p = \frac{1}{3}\sqrt{\frac{3\mathfrak{d}'}{A} - 4\rho^2}$$

The corresponding lines of steepest descent are at an angle of 45° to the axes (see Fig. 5).

Case A 3: $\mathfrak{d}' = \frac{4}{3} A\rho^2$.

In this case, a special saddle point exists at

$$n = -\frac{2}{3} i\rho \tag{15}$$

at which both dv/dn and $d^2v/dn^2 = iA(6n + 4i\rho)$ vanish. In order to calculate v in the vicinity of this point, polar coordinates r, α around the saddle point are introduced:

$$n = -\frac{2}{3} i\rho + re^{i\alpha}$$

Then,

$$\begin{aligned} v &= i(-\mathfrak{d}'n + An^3 + 2i\rho An^2) \\ &= iA\left(-\frac{4}{3}\rho^2 n + 2i\rho n^2 + n^3\right) \\ &= v_p + iAr^3 e^{i3\alpha} \end{aligned}$$

with

$$v_p = -\frac{8}{27} A\rho^3$$

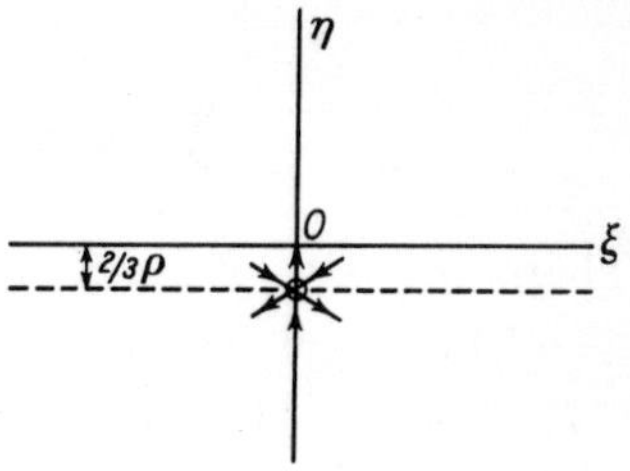

Fig. 6.

Thus,

$$X = X_p - Ar^3 \sin 3\alpha$$

Figure 6 shows this special saddle point of higher order, and the character of the lines of descent through it.

The two saddle points, which are at first on the imaginary axis, move closer together with increasing time, come together into a special saddle point when

$$\mathfrak{d}' = \frac{4}{3} A\rho^2 \qquad \left(\text{that is, } \Theta = \frac{n_2}{n_0} + \frac{4}{3} A\rho^2\right)$$

and then move apart symmetrically about the imaginary axis.

B. Saddle points far from the origin

Consider the n-plane for large n, and neglect n_0^2 compared with n^2. Then Eq. (2) becomes

$$\mu^2 = 1 + \frac{a^2}{n_0^2 - 2in\rho - n^2} \sim 1 - \frac{a^2}{n(2i\rho + n)}$$

or, since the second part is very small,

$$\mu = 1 - \frac{a^2}{2} \frac{1}{n(2i\rho + n)} \tag{16}$$

Formula (4) then becomes

$$v = -in(\Theta - \mu) = -in\mathfrak{d} - i\frac{a^2}{2}\frac{1}{2i\rho + n}$$

where $\Theta - 1 = \mathfrak{d}$ [see Eq. (4b)]. The saddle points are given by

$$\frac{dv}{dn} = 0, \qquad \mathfrak{d} - \frac{a^2}{2}\frac{1}{(2i\rho + n)^2} = 0$$

Therefore,

$$n_p = -2i\rho \pm \xi_p \qquad \xi_p = \frac{a}{\sqrt{2\mathfrak{d}}} \tag{17}$$

Thus there are two saddle points, symmetric about the η-axis, on the straight line $\eta = -2\rho$. One can write v as

$$v = -i\frac{a^2}{2}\left(\frac{n}{\xi_p^2} + \frac{1}{2i\rho + n}\right)$$

The equipotentials of X through n_p are the lines parallel to the axes. (Along the whole straight line $\eta = -2\rho$, $X = -2\rho\mathfrak{d}$, within the limits in which the approximations are valid.) The lines of steepest descent are inclined at 45° (see Fig. 7). For $\mathfrak{d} = 0$ the saddle points are at infinity on the line $\eta = -2\rho$, and with increasing $\mathfrak{d}$ they move along this line toward values of smaller $|\xi|$. When $\mathfrak{d}$ gets large enough, so that ξ_p is no longer large compared with n_0, i.e., when the saddle point comes near to the branch line, then the approximation loses its validity. One can show that the saddle points leave the line $\eta = -2\rho$, and move along the curve shown in Fig. 7 toward the branch line.

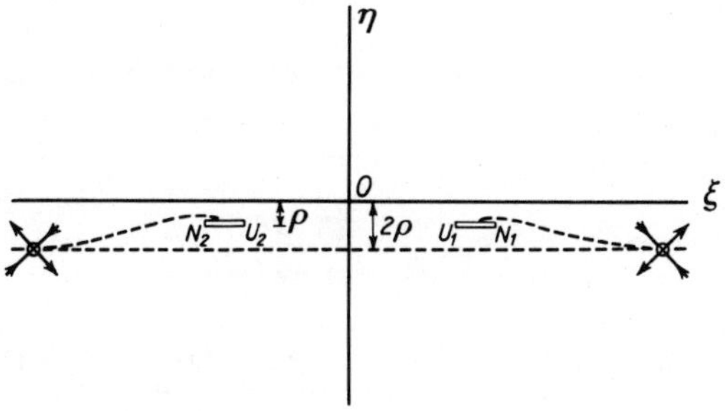

FIG. 7. Key: ————, path.

For very short times $\mathfrak{d}$ (Θ nearly equal to 1), there are two other saddle points which are on the imaginary axis on both sides of the origin, and which move closer to the real axis with increasing time Θ. These are the saddle points which we found near the origin for slightly greater times in Case A 1. Their exact location is not important.

Orders of Magnitude

This is the time to make some statements about the orders of magnitude of the various constants entering the formulas.

Suppose the depth inside the dispersive medium is

$$x = 1 \text{ cm}.$$

Let the wavelength of the incident signal, measured in air be

$$\lambda_0 = 0.5\,\mu = 5 \times 10^{-5} \text{ cm}.$$

then the frequency is

$$\nu = \frac{2\pi c}{\lambda_0} = \frac{2 \times 10^{11}}{5 \times 10^{-5}} = 4 \times 10^{15}$$

The characteristic frequency of the medium is taken as

$$n_0 = 10\,\nu = 4 \times 10^{16}$$

Let the index of refraction of the medium at the frequency ν be

$$\mu = 1.5$$

This information, together with the assumption of zero absorption ($\rho = 0$) allows a calculation of the order of magnitude of a^2.

According to Eq. (2′),

$$\mu^2 = 1 + \frac{a^2}{n_0{}^2 - \nu^2}$$

$$a^2 = (\mu^2 - 1)\left[\left(\frac{n_0}{\nu}\right)^2 - 1\right]\nu^2 = 1.25 \times 99 \times \nu^2 = 1.24 \times n_0{}^2$$

Thus, a is neady equal to n_0. Therefore,

$$n_2 = \sqrt{n_0{}^2 + a^2} = 1.5\,n_0 = 6 \times 10^{16}$$

The coefficient A was defined by

$$A = \frac{a^2}{2n_0{}^3 n_2} \sim \frac{a^5}{3n_0{}^4}, \qquad A \sim \frac{1}{5} \times 10^{-33}$$

It is also worthwhile giving some data on the order of magnitude of the coefficient ρ according to Goldhammer, in *Dispersion und Absorption des Lichtes.*[2] On p. 126 of that book is given data on the order of magnitude of the logarithmic decrement γ for several materials. This decrement is related to ρ by the equation

$$\rho = \frac{\gamma n}{2\pi}$$

Experiments with eosine and fuchsine give

$$\gamma = 0.45$$

For mercury, $\gamma = 0.8$, while for iodine the damping (loc. cit. p. 57) is very small.

---

[2] Goldhammer, "Dispersion und Absorption des Lichtes." Leipzig, 1913.

The following table gives the corresponding values of ρ.

γ	0.06	0.3	0.45	0.6	0.9
ρ/n_0	10^{-2}	5×10^{-2}	7.5×10^{-2}	10^{-1}	1.5×10^{-1}

In all ordinary cases, ρ^2 is therefore small compared with $n_0{}^2$, being approximately

$$\rho^2 = 5 \times 10^{-3}\, n_0{}^2$$

4. Successive Motion of the Saddle Points as a Function of Time. Choice of the Path of Integration

The following Figs. 8—14 show the view of the complex plane for several different times. Only one half plane is shown, but one can easily see that the two points $n = \pm\, \xi + i\eta$ which are symmetrical about the imaginary axis correspond to the value $v = X \pm iY$,

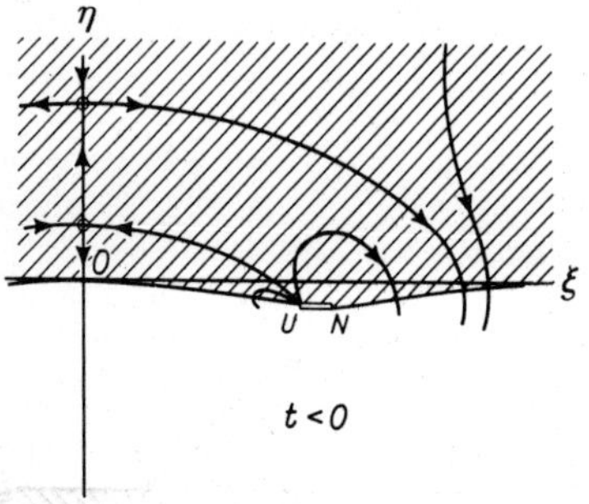

FIG. 8.

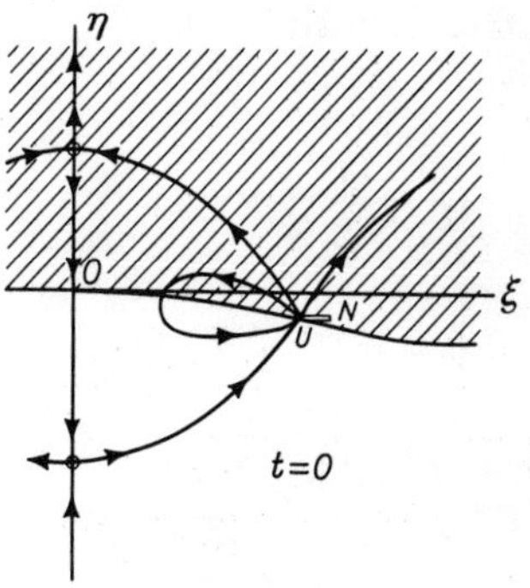

FIG. 9.

so that the figure is symmetrical about the imaginary axis. In the shaded regions, X is negative. The most important lines of steepest descent are drawn in. They start from the points where X is negatively infinite and go to the points where X is positively infinite.

These points are the two points U and (except for $\mathfrak{t} = 0$) the point at infinity on the imaginary axis. It is probably worthwhile reminding the reader of the notation.

$$\Theta = \frac{ct}{x} \qquad t - \frac{x}{c} = \mathfrak{t}$$

$$\Theta - 1 = \mathfrak{d} \qquad \frac{x}{c}\mathfrak{d} = \mathfrak{t}$$

For $t < (x/c)$ everything is at rest; the integral vanishes. The first forerunners of the signal arrive with the velocity c, that is, at the time $\mathfrak{t} = 0$ (compare Chapter II).

Figure 8 shows the picture of the complex plane for $\mathfrak{t} < 0$. The path of integration can be taken to infinity in the direction of the positive imaginary axis. The integral vanishes, since X is negatively infinite there.

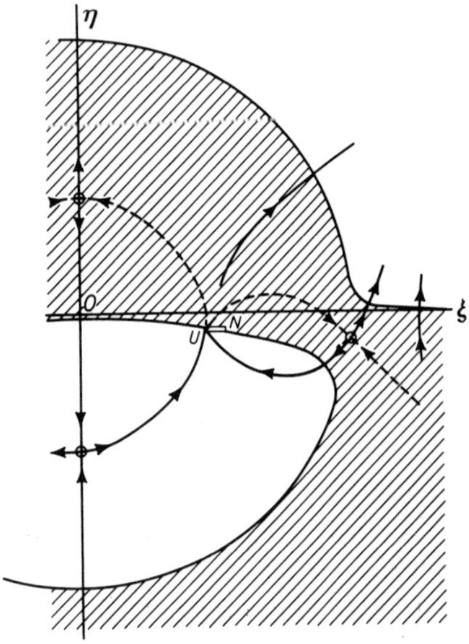

FIG. 10. Key: – – – –, path of integration.

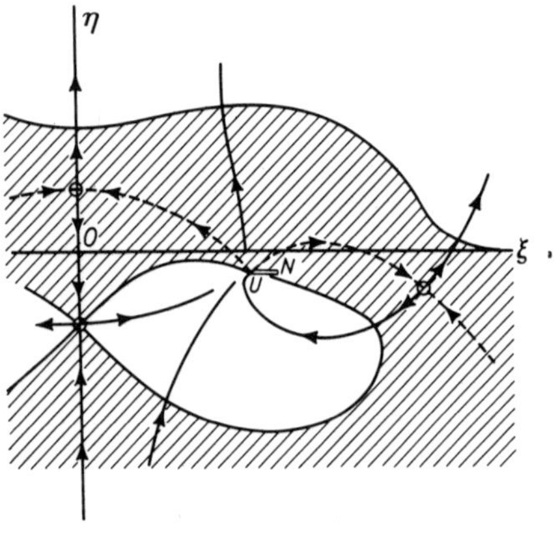

FIG. 11.

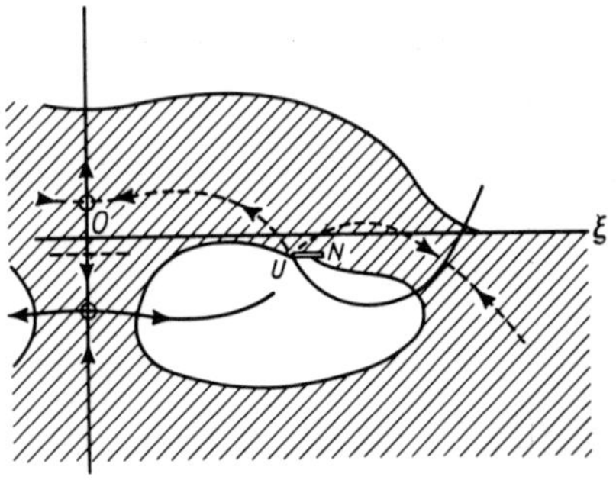

FIG. 12.

For the time $t = 0$, shown in Fig. 9, the circle with infinite radius is part of the curve $X = 0$. Here one can still deform the path in the upper half plane to infinity, but the integral now vanishes as $1/(n - \nu)$, rather than exponentially.

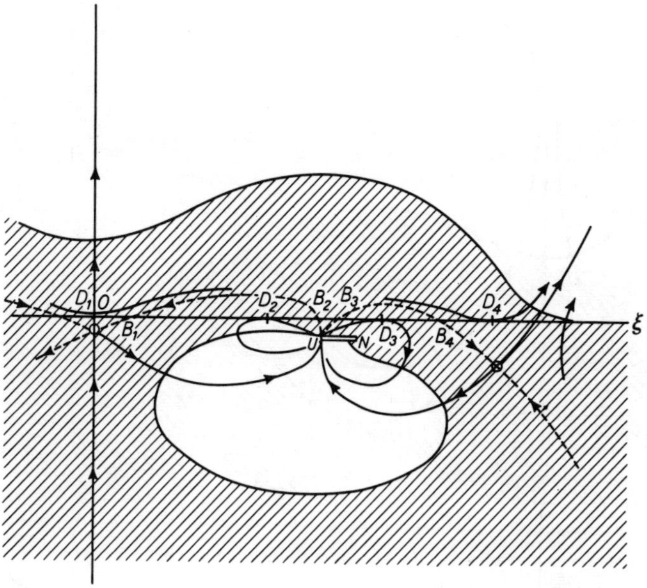

FIG. 13.

For $t > 0$, one can see from Figs. 10—14 the changes in the complex plane. From one section in which X has large negative values, one goes over a saddle point to another such section. The path of integration will be deformed so that it stays in such sections for a large part of its path, since the integral is practically zero there. Then, one only has to evaluate the integral near the saddle point, and, in fact, it is best to choose a line of steepest descent through the saddle point. This path of integration is shown in the figures, and its change with time is easily followed.

Near the saddle points, it is easier to do the integration if the saddle points are not too near the cuts UN or the point $n = \nu$. Then one can replace the path of integration by its tangent line through the saddle point, and consider $1/(n - \nu)$ as constant; thus one gets elementary integrals to perform (see Section 5). With these given conditions, the integration gives results corresponding to forerunners, whose amplitude is exceedingly small compared to the final amplitude of the signal.

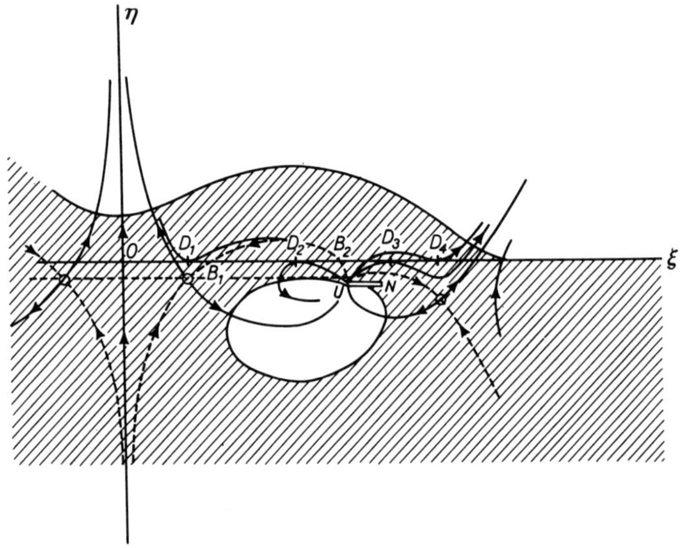

FIG. 14.

Now, to see what happens when the path of integration comes near the point $n = \nu$ (ν real). This point is taken between the origin and the branch line, $0 < \nu < n_0$. This is the case calculated earlier when orders of magnitude were considered: the signal was in the visible part of the spectrum propagating in a medium whose characteristic frequency was in the ultraviolet. The opposite case $\nu > n$ would give analogous results.

With increasing time, the path of integration is first above and to the left of the pole ν, then passes through it, and finally ends up to the right and below it. One must then add a curve around the pole [Figs. (15a, b, c)]. In the first case [Fig. (15a)], the integration gives an oscillating part whose amplitude increases to about 1/2 the final amplitude [Fig. (15b)]. Then one must add together a constant oscillating expression with a final amplitude which comes from a term representing the added curve about ν, and a negative term whose amplitude decreases from 1/2 the final amplitude to very small values, representing the other part of the path of integration. Figures 16 and 17 illustrate these several expressions and their superposition.

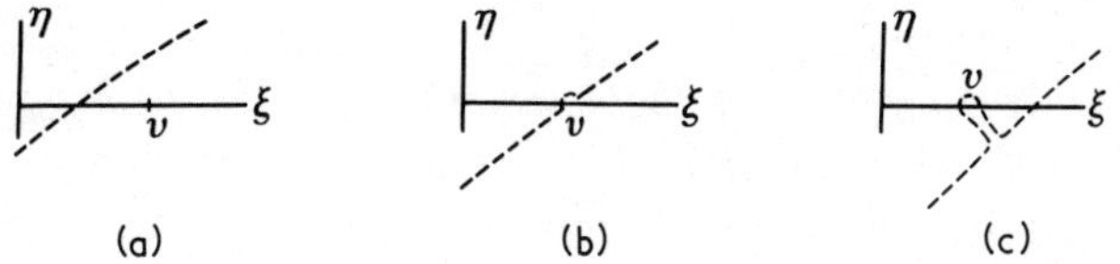

FIG. 15.

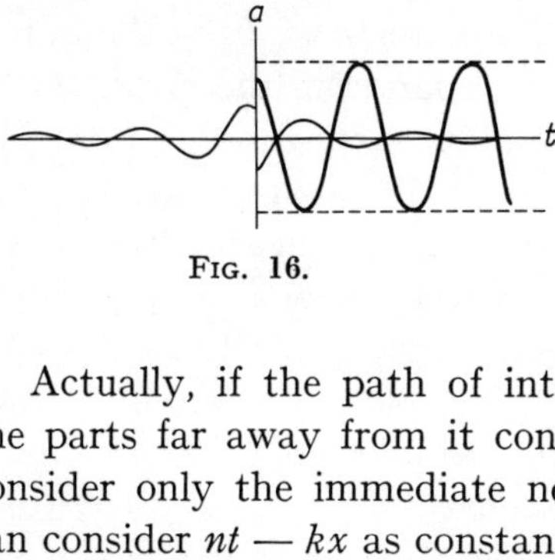

FIG. 16.

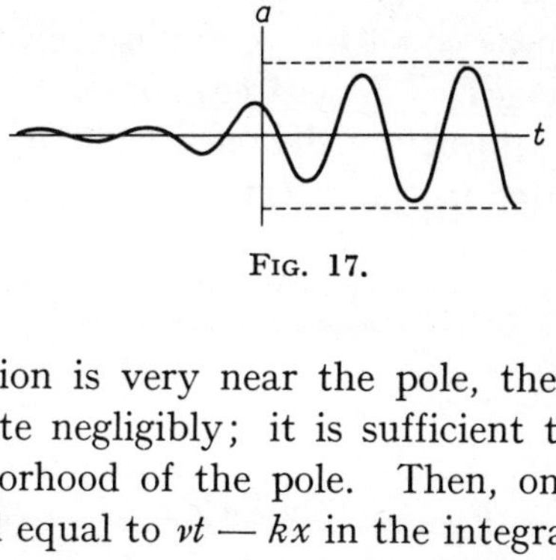

FIG. 17.

Actually, if the path of integration is very near the pole, then the parts far away from it contribute negligibly; it is sufficient to consider only the immediate neighborhood of the pole. Then, one can consider $nt - kx$ as constant and equal to $\nu t - kx$ in the integral

$$\frac{1}{2\pi} \operatorname{Re} \int \frac{e^{-i(nt-kx)}}{n-\nu} dn$$

where (see Eq. 7)

$$k = \frac{2\pi}{\lambda}(1 + i\kappa)$$

If ρ, ω are polar coordinates about ν, then

$$\frac{dn}{n-\nu} = i d\omega$$

and for the integral, it follows that

$$\mathrm{Re}\left[ie^{-i\left(\nu t - \frac{2\pi}{\lambda}x\right)}e^{-\frac{2\pi\kappa}{\lambda}x}\frac{1}{2\pi}\int d\omega\right] = e^{-2\pi\kappa\frac{x}{\lambda}}\sin\left(\nu t - 2\pi\frac{x}{\lambda}\right)\frac{\omega}{2\pi}$$

For the complete curve about the pole, $\omega/2\pi = 1$. The first term thus gives the final oscillation. For the path in Fig. 15b, one has $\omega/2\pi = \frac{1}{2}$, which proves the previous statement. The complete calculation of the integration near the pole will not be given here, since it is quite tedious and does not give anything more than the remarks already made.

Thus, it is seen that *at that moment when the path of integration reaches the pole, the intensity of the oscillation increases very rapidly*; previously, it was very small (compare further with the order of magnitude of the forerunners) and it now gets the magnitude of the final intensity. This moment, marking the arrival of the signal, permits one *to define a signal velocity*. This velocity will be shown to be equal to the group velocity, if the path is far from the branch line, i.e., if the frequency of the signal is far from the characteristic frequency of the medium. The saddle point C moves with increasing time in the direction of increasing ξ (Fig. 18) along a straight line, which is parallel to the real axis and near it. ($CD = \frac{2}{3}\rho$ is very small compared with ξ_p, cf. Fig. 5.) Of the lines of descent through the saddle point which are at angles of 45°, one is the path of integration; it cuts the real axis at B. If the lines of descent are drawn in the neighborhood of the saddle point, then it is seen that one of them touches the real axis at the point D, which has the same abscissa as the saddle point C.

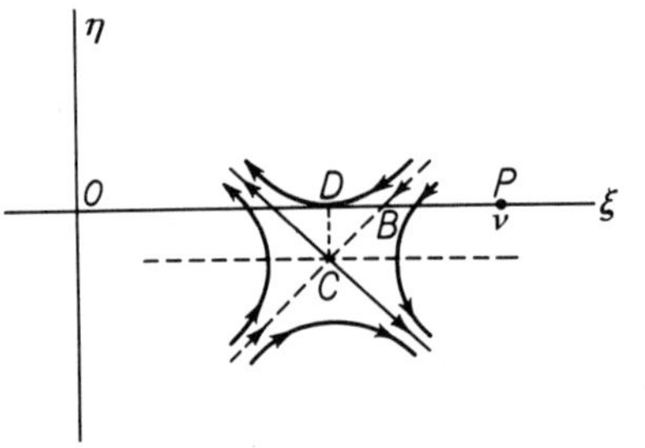

FIG. 18.

By definition, the time of arrival of the signal is the time when B arrives at the pole P. The distance $DB = CD$ is very small. It will be shown that the signal arrives *with a velocity exactly equal to the group velocity*, if the arrival of the signal is defined as the time when the *point D reaches the pole P*.

Actually, on the real axis (n real), $k = k_r + ik_i$; if real and imaginary parts are separated, then

$$w = -i(nt - kx) = -k_i x - i(nt - k_r x) = \frac{x}{c}(X + iY)$$

At D, the real axis is tangent to a line of descent of X, and the direction perpendicular to it is an equipotential for X:

$$\frac{\partial X}{\partial \eta} = 0 = -\frac{\partial Y}{\partial \xi}$$

thus

$$t - \frac{dk_r}{dn} x = 0$$

or

$$t - \frac{x}{U} = 0$$

where U is the group velocity. Now, the abscissa of the pole P is equal to ν, the frequency of the signal. Let U_ν be the group velocity corresponding to ν; the pole P reaches D at a time $t = x/U_\nu$ where x is the depth attained by the signal. If this defines the time of arrival of the signal, then this means that the signal propagates with the group velocity.

Concerning the velocity of propagation of a signal whose frequency is in the region of anomalous dispersion, see Section 6.

The signal velocity thus defines the moment of arrival of the signal with noticeable amplitude, whereas the phase velocity only determines the arrangement of the phases of the signal as explained in Chapter II, Section 4.

5. The Forerunners

In the previous paragraphs, the positions of the saddle points were calculated and it was shown how the path of integration passes through them; now the integration near the saddle points will be carried out. While the time when the path of integration passes over the pole provides the signal velocity, the integration near the saddle points will give secondary parts, the forerunners, whose intensity is very weak compared with that of the signal. The calculation is performed in the same order in which the positions of the saddle points were designated in Section 3.

A. Saddle points near the origin

Case A 1

For $\mathfrak{d}' < \frac{4}{3} A\rho^2$, two saddle points were found on the imaginary axis. The path of integration goes through the saddle point with ordinate [see formula (13), and Fig. 4]

$$\eta_p = -\frac{2}{3}\rho + \frac{1}{3}\sqrt{4\rho^2 - \frac{3\mathfrak{d}'}{A}}$$

parallel to the real axis. Near the saddle point,

$$n = i\eta_p + \xi$$

where ξ denotes a small real quantity; this function can be expanded near this saddle point by using Eq. (12). The first order parts vanish ($dv/dn = 0$ at the saddle point) and the second order parts are real since one stays on a line of descent of X (i.e., on a curve Y = constant). Then, one finds

$$v = v_p - B\xi^2$$

where

$$v_p = \eta_p[\mathfrak{d}' + A\eta_p(\eta_p + 2\rho)]$$

$$B = A(3\eta_p + 2\rho)$$

v_p, the value of the function v at the saddle point, is real; $v_p = X_p$, $Y_p = 0$, which is something which will be used later. This result is actually easily understood, and is valid even for saddle points far from the origin, for which the approximate formula (11) is not exact. The saddle point lies on the imaginary axis, and the line of descent which is used as a path of integration goes through the point and is symmetric about the imaginary axis. On this curve Y must be, firstly, constant (Section 1), and secondly, it must have the same value at points which lie symmetrically about the imaginary axis (compare the beginning of Section 4); thus it must necessarily be that $Y = 0$.

Now, the integral f near the saddle point must be evaluated.

$$f = \frac{1}{2\pi} \operatorname{Re} \int \frac{e^{(x/c)\nu}}{n - \nu} dn = \frac{e^{(x/c)\nu_p}}{2\pi} \int_{+\varepsilon}^{-\varepsilon} \frac{e^{-(x/c)B\xi^2}}{n - \nu} d\xi \tag{18}$$

In order that the approximate method should be valid, the limits $\pm \varepsilon$, between which the integral is taken, must be small compared with the other magnitudes in the n-plane, such as n_0. At the end of Section 3, the following orders of magnitude were shown to be admissible.

$$\nu = 4 \times 10^{15}, \qquad n_0 = 4 \times 10^{16}, \qquad A = \frac{1}{5} \times 10^{-33}$$

On the other hand, the approximate formula for the index of refraction requires that at the saddle point $\eta_p{}^2$ is much smaller than $n_0{}^2$. If one takes $\eta_p = 2 \times 10^{-2} n_0 \sim 10^{15}$, one finds that

$$B = 3A\eta_p = \frac{3}{5} \times 10^{15-33} = \frac{3}{5} \times 10^{-18}$$

and

$$\frac{x}{c} B = x \frac{3}{3 \times 5} \times 10^{-18-10} = 2x \times 10^{-29}$$

The approximation will be valid, if one can find a value ε so much smaller than n_0 that $\exp\{-(x/c)B\varepsilon^2\}$ is practically zero. It is sufficient to require that

$$\frac{x}{c} B\varepsilon^2 = 5$$

If the depth traversed by the light $x = 1$ cm., this requires that:

$$2 \times \varepsilon^2 \times 10^{-29} = 5, \qquad \varepsilon^2 = 25 \times 10^{28}$$

$$\varepsilon = 5 \times 10^{14} = \frac{n_0}{100}$$

For a depth $x = 100$ cm., one finds that $\varepsilon = 5 \times 10^{13} = n_0/1000$. These values are admissible for the calculation.

$n - \nu$ will be considered constant in these limits:

$$\frac{1}{n-\nu} = \frac{1}{i\eta_p - \nu} = -\frac{\nu + i\eta_p}{\nu^2 + \eta_p{}^2}$$

and then the integral

$$\frac{1}{2\pi}\int_{+\varepsilon}^{-\varepsilon} e^{-(x/c)B\xi^2}\,d\xi = -\frac{1}{2\pi}\sqrt{\frac{\pi c}{Bx}} = -\frac{1}{2}\sqrt{\frac{c}{\pi Bx}}$$

Taking the real part, one finally finds from Eq. (18),

$$f = \frac{\nu}{2(\nu^2 + \eta_p{}^2)}\sqrt{\frac{c}{\pi Bx}}\, e^{(x/c)v_p}$$

Now to investigate the order of magnitude of f and its variation with time. The square root is of order of magnitude $\frac{4}{3} \times 10^{14}$, and increases slowly; the first factor is of order $1/2\nu$, in other words about $\frac{1}{8} \times 10^{-15}$; The product of the two factors is about 1/60 and increases with time. The behavior of the exponent must still be considered. Now

$$\frac{x}{c} v_p = \frac{x}{c}\,[\eta_p\mathfrak{d}' + A\eta_p{}^2(\eta_p + 2\rho)]$$

where

$$\eta_p = -\frac{2}{3}\rho + \frac{1}{3}\sqrt{4\rho^2 - \frac{3\mathfrak{d}'}{A}}$$

η_p is thus of order of magnitude $\sqrt{|\mathfrak{d}'|/3A}$, which gives

$$\frac{x}{c} v_p \sim \frac{2}{3}\frac{x}{c}\eta_p\mathfrak{d}'$$

This is a negative number of large absolute value [$(x/c)\mathfrak{d}' < 0$, η_p large], which approaches zero for $\mathfrak{d}' = 0$. The approximation does not give the exact variation for $\mathfrak{d}' = 0$.

All in all, the function f is at first nearly zero, then increases taking on the still small value of

$$f_{\mathfrak{d}'=0} = \frac{1}{2\nu}\sqrt{\frac{c}{2\pi\rho x A}}$$

for $\mathfrak{d}' = 0$. The value of f for times $\mathfrak{d}' \approx \frac{4}{3}A\rho^2$ will not be calculated here. A slow transition occurs from the nonoscillatory solution found here to the oscillating function which will be found for $\mathfrak{d}' > \frac{4}{3}A\rho^2$. Throughout this region, however, f retains the order of magnitude of $f_{\mathfrak{d}'=0}$.

Case A 2

If $\mathfrak{d}' > \frac{4}{3}A\rho^2$, then there are two saddle points symmetric about the imaginary axis (see Fig. 5):

$$n = -i\frac{2}{3}\rho \pm \xi_p$$

(see formula 14). The path of integration through them is in the direction of straight lines at 45°. Thus, near these saddle points,

$$n = -i\frac{2}{3}\rho \pm \xi_p + (1 \pm i)\varepsilon$$

thus

$$dn = (1 \pm i)d\varepsilon = \sqrt{2}\, e^{\pm i\pi/4}\, d\varepsilon$$

As in the previously handled case, the exponent v near the saddle point takes on the form

$$v = v_p - C\varepsilon^2$$

One finds

$$v_p = -\mathfrak{d}'\left(\frac{2}{3}\rho \pm i\xi_p\right) + iA\left(\pm \xi_p - i\frac{2}{3}\rho\right)^2\left(\pm \xi_p + i\frac{4}{3}\rho\right)$$

$$v_p = X_p \pm iY_p, \qquad C = 6A\,\xi_p$$

$$X_p = \frac{2}{3}\rho\left(-\mathfrak{d}' + \frac{9}{8}A\rho^2\right), \qquad Y_p = \xi_p\left[-\mathfrak{d}' + A\left(\xi_p{}^2 + \frac{4}{3}\rho^2\right)\right]$$

It is still necessary to evaluate the integral

$$\frac{1}{2\pi}\,\mathrm{Re}\int \frac{e^{(\lambda/c)v}}{n-\nu}\,dn$$

in the immediate neighborhood of the above mentioned saddle points. The coefficient C has the same order of magnitude as the coefficient B in the previous case. In the first approximation, the factor $1/(n-\nu)$ is considered as constant for each of the integrals at the saddle points, and is taken in front of the integral sign along with a factor of value $e^{(x/c)v_p}$. The remaining integral for one or the other of the saddle points is

$$\frac{1}{2\pi}\sqrt{2}\,e^{\pm i\pi/4}\int_{+\alpha}^{-\alpha} e^{-(x/c)C\varepsilon^2}\,d\varepsilon$$

where α has a small value. Considering the magnitude of C, the integral has the same value as it would have if α were infinite, namely

$$-\frac{1}{2\pi}\sqrt{2}\,e^{\pm i\pi/4}\sqrt{\pi}\sqrt{\frac{c}{xC}} = -\frac{1}{2}\,e^{\pm i\pi/4}\sqrt{\frac{c}{3\pi\xi_p xA}}$$

replacing C by its equivalent. Thus, all in all, the integration near the saddle points gives

$$f = -\frac{1}{2}\sqrt{\frac{c}{3\pi\xi_p xA}}\times$$
$$\mathrm{Re}\left[\frac{e^{\frac{x}{c}(X_p+iY_p)}}{-i\frac{2}{3}\rho+\xi_p-\nu}\,e^{i\pi/4}+\frac{e^{\frac{x}{c}(X_p-iY_p)}}{-i\frac{2}{3}\rho-\xi_p-\nu}\,e^{-i\pi/4}\right]$$

After some elementary manipulations one finally gets

$$f = \frac{\nu\sqrt{\dfrac{c}{2\pi\xi_p xA}}\,e^{\frac{x}{c}X_p}}{\left(\nu^2+\xi_p{}^2+\frac{4}{9}\rho^2\right)^2-4\nu^2\xi_p{}^2}\times$$

$$\left[\left(\nu^2-\xi_p{}^2+\frac{4}{9}\rho^2\right)\cos\left(\frac{\pi}{4}+\frac{x}{c}Y_p\right)+\frac{4}{3}\rho\xi_p\sin\left(\frac{\pi}{4}+\frac{x}{c}Y_p\right)\right] \tag{19}$$

The exponent $(x/c)X_p$ is always negative, its absolute value increases with time approximately as

$$+\frac{2}{3}(x/c)\rho\mathfrak{d}' = +\frac{2}{3}\rho\mathfrak{t}'$$

The value of $\exp\{(x/c)X_p\}$, which at first ($\mathfrak{d}' = 0$) is nearly 1, decreases finally and approaches zero, as the saddle points near the branch line. The square root varies in the same way with the time. The other factor will be slightly simplified (so that its behavior can be better seen) by neglecting ρ^2 with respect to $\nu^2 - \xi_p^2$, which is always valid except when the saddle point is near the pole ν. One then finds

$$f = \frac{\nu}{\nu^2 - \xi_p^2}\sqrt{\frac{c}{3\pi\xi_p xA}}\, e^{\frac{x}{c}X_p} \times$$

$$\left[\cos\left(\frac{\pi}{4} + \frac{x}{c}Y_p\right) + \frac{4}{3}\rho\frac{\xi_p}{\nu^2 - \xi_p^2}\sin\left(\frac{\pi}{4} + \frac{x}{c}Y_p\right)\right] \tag{19'}$$

One sees that in general the cosine term is much greater then the sine term, but when the saddle point approaches the pole, a change in phase occurs, since the sine term is no longer negligible. The factor $\nu/(\nu^2 - \xi_p^2)$ which is usually of the order $1/\nu$, that is, very small, becomes very large when the saddle point nears the pole.

Now it is appropriate to find the instantaneous frequency $\omega = 2\pi/T$ of this oscillation, which is arbitrarily defined as the time derivative of the phase, at least when the cosine part dominates, i.e., when ξ_p deviates greatly from ν:

$$\omega = \frac{d}{dt}\left(\frac{\pi}{4} + \frac{x}{c}Y_p\right) = \frac{dY_p}{d\theta} = \frac{dY_p}{d\mathfrak{d}'}$$

thus

$$\xi_p^2 = \frac{1}{9}\left(\frac{3\mathfrak{d}'}{A} - 4\rho^2\right) = \frac{1}{3}\frac{\mathfrak{d}'}{A}$$

if ρ^2 can be neglected in comparison with $\mathfrak{d}'/A$. Thus

$$Y_p = -\frac{2}{3}\xi_p\mathfrak{d}' = -\frac{2\sqrt{3}\,\mathfrak{d}'^{3/2}}{9\,A^{1/2}}$$

$$\omega = -\frac{\sqrt{3}}{3} \times \frac{\mathfrak{d}'^{1/2}}{A^{1/2}} = -\xi_p$$

The instantaneous frequency is thus equal to the abscissa ξ_p of the saddle point, i.e., according to the above (the end of Section 4) it is equal to the frequency of an oscillation whose group velocity is x/t.

The order of magnitude of the amplitude of the wave motion will be calculated using the same magnitudes assumed in the previous case:

$$\xi_p = 2 \times 10^{-2} n_0 = 10^{15}$$

$$C = 2B, \qquad \frac{1}{2}\frac{x}{c} C = 2x \times 10^{-29}$$

The amplitude is, except for the exponential factor

$$\frac{1}{\nu}\sqrt{\frac{2c}{\pi C x}} = \frac{1}{30}$$

The forerunners thus have an amplitude of the order 1/30, i.e. an intensity of about 1/1000 of that of the signal. This intensity, however, depends directly on the spectral distribution of the initial signal. Actually, the factor

$$\frac{\nu}{\nu^2 - \xi_p{}^2}$$

occurs in the expression for the amplitude of the oscillation under consideration, which, except for the numerical factor $-1/\pi$, gives the amplitude of the oscillation of the frequency ξ_p in the original signal (Chapter II, Section 2):

$$\frac{\nu}{\nu^2 - \xi_p{}^2} = -\pi \frac{2}{\tau} \frac{1}{\xi_p{}^2 - (2\pi/\tau)^2}$$

The expression (19′) can also be written in another form, in which only the values of x and $\mathfrak{t}'$ occur. This representation is approximate only for saddle points which do not lie too near the origin or the pole ν. The previous approximate relation is used

$$\xi_p = \frac{1}{3}\sqrt{\frac{3\mathfrak{d}'}{A}} = \sqrt{\frac{c\mathfrak{t}'}{3Ax}}$$

and we thus get from Eq. (19):

$$f = \frac{1}{\sqrt{\pi}}\left(\frac{c}{3Ax\mathfrak{t}'}\right)^{1/4}\cdot\frac{\nu}{\nu^2 - c\mathfrak{t}'/3Ax}\,e^{-(2/3)\rho\mathfrak{t}'}\times$$
$$\left[\cos\left(\frac{2}{3}\sqrt{\frac{c}{3Ax}}\,\mathfrak{t}'^{3/2} - \frac{\pi}{4}\right) - \frac{\frac{4}{3}\rho\sqrt{c\mathfrak{t}'/3Ax}}{\nu^2 - c\mathfrak{t}'/3Ax}\sin\left(\frac{2}{3}\sqrt{\frac{c}{3Ax}}\,\mathfrak{t}'^{3/2} - \frac{\pi}{4}\right)\right]$$

(19″)

The integration around the saddle points near the origin has thus revealed an oscillatory motion of the following kind: until times near $\mathfrak{t}' = (x/c)\mathfrak{d}' = 0$ $(t = xn_2/n_0c)$, no noticeable motion; for $\mathfrak{t}'$ nearly zero, a small deflection; then for $\mathfrak{t}' > 0$, an oscillatory motion with small amplitude whose frequency increases from zero. The amplitude increases quickly, as the frequency of these forerunners approaches that of the signal. The signal approaches with the group velocity and quickly takes on its final amplitude. It is still influenced for some time by the forerunners whose amplitude decreases quickly while their frequency continues to increase. As their frequency approaches the characteristic frequency of the oscillating electrons in the medium, their amplitude becomes unnoticeable.

This applies for the case where $0 < \nu < n_0$, i.e., for a visible signal and a characteristic frequency of the electrons in the ultraviolet.

The part of the forerunners which were just found will be called the second forerunners; the integration around the saddle points lying far from the imaginary axis will produce the first forerunners.

B. Saddle points at a great distance

It was seen that for small times $\mathfrak{d}$ account must be taken of one saddle point on the imaginary axis and two additional ones symmetric about this axis at the points [see Eq. (17), and Fig. 7]

$$\xi_p = \pm\frac{a}{\sqrt{2\mathfrak{d}}}, \qquad \eta_p = -2\rho$$

The integration near the saddle point on the imaginary axis contributes a negligible amount, since it is a flat saddle point. It was already shown (Case A 1), that the integration near this point can be neglected except when the point is near the origin. It was also mentioned that on the line of descent through this saddle point, i.e., on the path of integration, Y vanishes.

Thus, only the two remaining saddle points through which the path of integration passes at 45° must be considered. Near these points,

$$n = -2i\rho \pm \xi_p + (1 \mp i)\varepsilon$$

$$dn = (1 \mp i)\, d\varepsilon = \sqrt{2}\, e^{\mp i \frac{\pi}{4}}\, d\varepsilon$$

and one can expand v as

$$v = v_\rho - D\varepsilon^2 = -\rho \frac{a^2}{\xi_p{}^2} \mp i \frac{a^2}{\xi_p} - \frac{a^2}{\xi_p{}^3}\varepsilon^2$$

For these saddle points, the limits $\pm \alpha$ in the integral

$$\frac{1}{2\pi} \operatorname{Re} \int_{+\alpha}^{-\alpha} \frac{e^{(x/c)v}}{n - \nu}\, dn$$

must be chosen in such a way, that $e^{-(x/c)D\varepsilon^2}$ vanishes at these limits. The approximations are valid if one can choose α so that it is small compared with ξ_p. In order to be able to give a numerical example of this, the following values are chosen:

$$\xi_p = 10 \times n_0, \qquad a = n_0 = 4 \times 10^{16}$$

$$D = \frac{a^2}{\xi_p{}^3} = \frac{1}{4} \times 10^{-16} \times 10^{-3} = \frac{1}{4} \times 10^{-19}$$

$$\frac{x}{c} D = 10^{-30}$$

The exponential is practically zero if $-(x/c)D\varepsilon^2 \approx -10$. Thus it is required that

$$10^{-30}\,\varepsilon^2 = 10, \qquad \varepsilon = 3 \times 10^{15}$$

Thus ε is of the order $\xi_p/100$, which is quite admissible. The approximation is valid if the abscissa ξ_p of the saddle point is greater than n_0

but not too great, as would be the case for times $\mathfrak{d}$ very near zero [see Eq. (17)].

If the factor $1/(n - \nu)$ is considered as constant and taken in front of the integral sign, then the integral

$$\int_{+\infty}^{-\infty} e^{-\frac{a^2}{\xi_p^3}\frac{x}{c}\varepsilon^2}\, d\varepsilon = -\frac{1}{a}\sqrt{\frac{c\pi\xi_p^2}{x}}$$

Depending on which saddle point is under consideration, it must be multiplied by

$$\frac{\sqrt{2}\, e^{\mp i\frac{\pi}{4}}\, e^{\frac{x}{c}v_p}}{n_p - \nu} = \sqrt{2}\,\frac{e^{-\rho\frac{a^2}{\xi_p^2}\frac{x}{c}}\, e^{\mp i\left(\frac{a^2}{\xi_p}\frac{x}{c}+\frac{\pi}{4}\right)}}{-2i\rho \pm \xi_p - \nu}$$

Then the two parts are added and the real part of the sum is taken, finally giving

$$\mathfrak{f} = -\sqrt{2}\,\frac{\nu}{a}\left(\frac{c}{\pi\xi_p x}\right)^{1/2} e^{-2\rho\mathfrak{t}}\cos\left(\frac{a^2}{\xi_p}\frac{x}{c}+\frac{\pi}{4}\right) \tag{20}$$

or replacing ξ_p everywhere by $\mathfrak{t}$, according to formula (17):

$$\mathfrak{f} = -\frac{\nu}{\sqrt{\pi a^3}}\left(\frac{2c}{x}\right)^{3/4} \mathfrak{t}^{1/4} e^{-2\rho\mathfrak{t}}\cos\left(a\sqrt{\frac{2x}{c}}\,\mathfrak{t}+\frac{\pi}{4}\right) \tag{20'}$$

The first forerunners thus arrive with the velocity of light in vacuum, since they begin at $\mathfrak{t} = t - (x/c) = 0$. Their period is at first very small, and increases steadily. If an instantaneous frequency is defined as was done for the second forerunners, then one can easily see that here too the frequency is equal to the abscissa ξ_p of the saddle point at any moment. The amplitude is at first zero, then increases, and (neglecting the damping) then decreases as

$$\mathfrak{t}^{1/4}\, e^{-2\rho\mathfrak{t}}$$

For the numerical example chosen, the amplitude of the first forerunners is found to be of the order of 2×10^{-3}, i.e., the intensity is of the order of 4×10^{-6}.

The approximations given here lose their validity for very small $\mathfrak{t}$, i.e., for very distant saddle points. This is because the first forerunners are actually given by the expression

$$f = \frac{\nu}{a} \sqrt{\frac{2c\mathfrak{t}}{x}}\, J_1\left(2a\sqrt{\frac{x\mathfrak{t}}{2c}}\right)$$

as Sommerfeld showed [Chapter II, Eq. (33)]. If one replaces the Bessel function by its asymptotic expansion, one gets formula (20′), and thus one sees that its validity is limited to not too small values of $\mathfrak{t}$. The factor $e^{-2\rho\mathfrak{t}}$ is missing because Sommerfeld's formula was derived under the condition $\rho = 0$. Returning to the magnitudes given at the end of Section 3, it is easy to see that in that example, ρ cannot be neglected compared with n_0.

6. Signal Velocity

In the preceeding paragraphs, the forerunners were calculated and it was shown by numerical examples that their intensity was very small compared with that of the actual signal. Now, the signal velocity will be discussed.

Near the end of Section 4, it was shown that at the moment when the path of integration meets the pole, the amplitude of the oscillation becomes appreciable — of the order of half the final amplitude. Thus, *the arrival of the signal can be arbitrarily defined as the moment when the path of integration reaches the pole* ν.

All of these considerations referred to the case in which ν was far different from n_0, that is, to the case of normal dispersion. It seems appropriate to retain the previous definition *in all cases, even if the signal has a period in the region of anomalous dispersion.*

Since ν is an actual frequency and thus is a positive real number, the pole ν is always on the ξ axis between 0 and $+\infty$.

Considering a signal as it is seen at a depth x at time t, and drawing the complex plane (Figs. 8—14), then the figure depends only on the magnitude

$$v = -in(\Theta - \mu) = X + iY$$

[compare Eq. (4)]; it is independent of the frequency ν of the signal; it is the same for a different depth x' at a time t' satisfying the relation [compare Eq. (4a)]

$$\Theta = \Theta', \qquad \frac{tc}{x} = \frac{t'c}{x'} \tag{21}$$

The positive real axis intersects the path of integration at the points $B_1, B_2, \ldots$ with the abscissa $\nu_1, \nu_2 \ldots$ (compare, for example, Figs. 13 and 14). According to the definition just introduced, a signal of frequency ν_1 will acquire an appreciable intensity at the time t corresponding to the figure. Relation (21) shows that the time t is proportional to the depth x; the signal thus propagates with constant signal velocity S. One has

$$t = \frac{x}{S}, \qquad \Theta = \frac{ct}{x} = \frac{c}{S}$$

The reduced time Θ gives the ratio of the velocity in vacuum to the signal velocity for a frequency ν_1. Figures 10—14 show the displacement of the points $B_1, B_2, \ldots$ with increasing Θ. A plot of $c/S = \Theta$ as ordinate versus $\nu_1, \nu_2 \ldots$ as abscissas, yields the curve shown in Fig. 19. The points B correspond to the points b having the same abscissas.

In Section 4 it was shown that for a point D (Fig. 18) in the complex plane, through which a line of descent for x is tangent to the real axis,

$$t = x/U, \qquad \Theta = c/U$$

where U is the group velocity for a frequency $\xi = OD$. In Fig. 19 the curve c/U is drawn, the points D corresponding to the points d.

In Figs. 10—14 it is easy to draw the complete set of lines of descent and to compare the positions of the points B and D. One then finds (see Section 4, Fig. 18), that a saddle point not too near the branch line is very near the two points B and D, which are themselves very close to each other (for instance, B and D of Fig. 18, B_1D_1 and B_4D_4 of Fig. 13, B_1D_1 of Fig. 14). This means, however, that far from the region of anomalous dispersion, the curves c/S and c/U

coincide: in other words, that the signal velocity is equal to the group velocity (cf. the end of Section 4). This no longer applies if the saddle point moves into the neighborhood of the branch line. Nevertheless, even then the corresponding positions of the points B and D give information about the unknown curve for the signal velocity from the known curve for the group velocity.

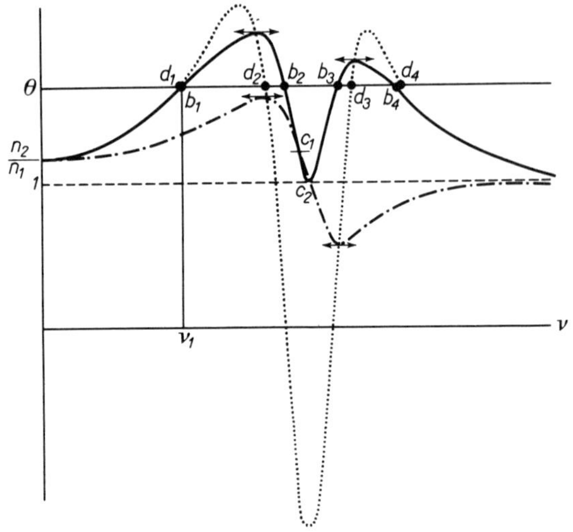

FIG. 19. Key: —·—·—, c/phase velocity $= c/W$; · · · ·, c/group velocity $= c/U$; ———, c/signal velocity $= c/S$.

At first, the path of integration intersects the real axis at two points B_3, B_4 between which lies one point D_3 (see Fig. 13). At one certain time, the path is tangent to the real axis and the points B_3, B_4, and D_3 coincide, as is also the case for points b_3, b_4, and d_3 in Fig. 19. From this time on, this part of the path of integration no longer touches the real axis (Fig. 14). This means the maxima of the curve c/S are the points of intersection of the curves c/S and c/U.

The path of integration, which is chosen as a line of descent through the saddle points, is made up of several parts, each of which goes through only one saddle point (Figs. 10—14):

Part 1: $+\infty > \xi > \xi_\infty$, from $+\infty$ to the point U_1

Part 2: $\xi_\infty > \xi > -\xi_\infty$, from U_1 to U_2

Part 3: $-\xi_\infty > \xi > -\infty$, from U_2 to $-\infty$.

For Case A 2 (Section 3), where

$$\mathfrak{d}' > \frac{4}{3} A \rho^2$$

part 2 of the path is itself split into two parts (Figs. 13 and 14).

The imaginary part Y of the exponent v remains constant along the path of integration which is a line of steepest descent for X; thus, for each part,

$$Y = Y_p$$

In Section 5 where the integrals near the saddle points were calculated, the corresponding values of Y were given:

Part 1: Saddle point far from the origin (Section 5, Case B):

$$Y_p = -\frac{a^2}{\xi_p} = -a\sqrt{2\mathfrak{d}}$$

Part 2: Saddle point near the origin:

$$\text{(22)} \quad \begin{aligned} &\text{Case A 1,} \quad \mathfrak{d}' \leqslant \frac{4}{3} A\rho^2\colon\ Y_p = 0 \\ &\text{Case A 2,} \quad \mathfrak{d}' > \frac{4}{3} A\rho^2\colon\ Y_p = \xi_p\left[-\mathfrak{d}' + A\left(\xi_p^2 + \frac{4}{3}\rho^2\right)\right] \\ &\qquad \left(\xi_p = \frac{1}{3}\sqrt{\frac{3\mathfrak{d}'}{A} - 4\rho^2}\right) \end{aligned}$$

The next step is to determine the points B_2 and B_3 where the path of integration cuts the real axis near the branch line UN (Fig. 13).

On the real axis (n real), Eq. (4) shows that

$$Y = -n(\Theta - \mu_r) = -n\left(\Theta - \frac{c}{W}\right) \tag{23}$$

where μ_r = index of refraction, W = phase velocity at the frequency n. The curve $\mu_r = c/W$ is known; it is also shown in Fig. 19. The points B_2, B_3 are those points on the real axis where Eq. (22) and Eq. (23) agree. In Case A 1, i.e., when

$$\mathfrak{d}' \leqslant \frac{4}{3} A\rho^2, \qquad \Theta \leqslant \frac{n_2}{n_0} + \frac{4}{3} A\rho^2$$

the second part of the path of integration requires that $Y = 0$; thus it cuts the real axis near the branch line at a point for which

$$\Theta - \frac{c}{W} = 0, \qquad \frac{c}{S} = \Theta = \frac{c}{W}$$

For these values of Θ, the curve c/S thus coincides with the curve c/W (see Fig. 19, the path from C_1 to C_2).

In particular, it can be seen that near n_0 there exists one frequency (point C_2) for which the signal propagates with the velocity of light in vacuum, and the corresponding index of refraction is unity:

$$c/W = c/S = 1$$

In all other cases (A 2 and B, and the path from c_2 to b_3 in Fig. 19),

$$Y < 0$$

on the path of integration. Thus, for the points of intersection with the real axis,

$$-n\left(\Theta - \frac{c}{W}\right) < 0, \qquad \Theta - \frac{c}{W} > 0$$

so that

$$c/S > c/W$$

and the curve for c/S lies above the curve for c/W. With this information the curve for c/S, which was to be investigated, can be drawn.

The signal velocity does not differ from the group velocity, except in the region of anomalous dispersion. There the group velocity becomes greater than the velocity in vacuum if the reciprocal $c/U < 1$;

it even becomes negative.[3] The signal velocity is always less than or at most equal to the velocity of light in vacuum. The curves for the group velocity and the signal velocity intersect at two points which, as was shown graphically, are maxima of the signal velocity.

Remembering that the definition of the signal velocity is somewhat arbitrary, it seems appropriate to draw a strip rather than a curve in Fig. 19 to represent the signal velocity, whose thickness indicates this arbitrariness. The signal does not arrive suddenly; there is a quick but still continuous transition from the very weak intensity of the forerunners to that corresponding to the signal. A detector set to detect an intensity equal to 1/4 the final intensity will detect the arrival of the signal in agreement with the above arbitrary definition; if the detector is more or less sensitive, then it will detect the arrival of the signal a little earlier or later.

7. Summary of Results

The results can be summarized in the following way: The propagation of a special kind of signal in a dispersive medium was investigated. It was found that after penetrating to a certain depth in the medium, the signal changes. The first forerunners arrive with a velocity c; their originally very small period increases continuously, their amplitude increases and, taking the damping into account, then decreases, until the period is equal to the characteristic period of the oscillating electrons. The second forerunners arrive with the velocity $c(n_2/n_0) < c$ determined by the dielectric constants; their period is at first very large and then decreases, while their amplitude behaves in a manner similar to that of the first forerunners. These two forerunners can partly overlap. In general, their amplitude is very small, but increases rapidly as their period approaches that of the signal. The signal arrives with the signal velocity; it is still deformed for some time thereafter by the overlapping forerunners. The time variation of the signal is schematically shown in Fig. 20 for the case in which

[3] See A. Schuster, "Einführung in die theoretische Optik." Leipzig, 1907. Naturally, the group velocity has a meaning only so long as it agrees with the signal velocity. The negative parts of the group velocity have no physical meaning.

the period of the signal is greater than the characteristic period of the electrons in the dispersive medium.

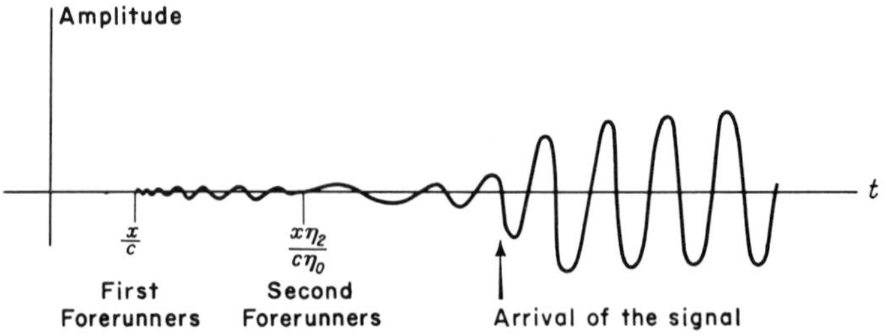

FIG. 20.

A few remarks about the dependence of the intensity of the forerunners on the depth should still be made. Let the part of the wave motion determined by a certain instantaneous frequency (see after Eq. 19′) arrive at a depth x_1 at time t_1 and at x_2 at time t_2. Then

$$\frac{t_1}{x_1} = \frac{t_2}{x_2}, \qquad \Theta_1 = \frac{t_1 c}{x_1} = \frac{t_2 c}{x_2} = \Theta_2$$

The value of the reduced time Θ which has the dimensions of a pure number determines the frequency of the wave motion independently of the depth. Also, the abscissa ξ_p of the saddle point is dependent on t and x only through the relationship in Θ. In order to compare the intensity of the forerunners of the same frequency at different *depths*, formulas (19), or (19′), and (20), which relate the quantities ξ, Θ, $\mathfrak{d}$, or $\mathfrak{d}'$, must be used. It is then seen that for a given period, the amplitude varies as

$$\frac{1}{\sqrt{x}} e^{-\frac{2}{3}\rho \frac{\mathfrak{d}'}{c} x} \qquad \text{for the second forerunners}$$

$$\frac{1}{\sqrt{x}} e^{-2\rho \frac{\mathfrak{d}}{c} x} \qquad \text{for the first forerunners}$$

The two forerunners thus experience a decrease in intensity, which is independent of the period and is inversely proportional to x, and besides this has an absorption which increases exponentially with depth. The latter is selective; the coefficient depends on the period, vanishing for a period of 0 or ∞.

The performance of the following experiment seems to be feasible. Send a signal into an absorbing medium. At a sufficient depth, the signal itself as well as these forerunners which are exponentially damped will be undetectable. One can detect only those forerunners with frequency 0 or ∞.

Although in this paper only the case of a material having one characteristic frequency and only one absorption band was treated, it is hoped that soon it will be possible to generalize this to the case of several absorption bands. Presently, it seems probable that in this case there will not be only two kinds of forerunners, but rather that between adjacent absorption bands there will be forerunners with periods lying between the bands. While it is pretty difficult to detect signals of periods 0 and ∞, the forerunners in the visible spectrum or its neighborhood could easily be detected.

8. The Method of the Stationary Phase Compared to the Saddle Point Method

Suppose one wishes to examine an integral of the form

$$\int \phi(n) \cos Y dn \qquad \text{or} \qquad \int \phi(n) e^{iY}\, dn$$

which is to be evaluated along the real n axis. Suppose ϕ is slowly varying everywhere. In those places where Y varies rapidly, $\cos Y$ or e^{iY} oscillates very rapidly and the integral is practically zero. It is therefore necessary to examine only those points on the real n-axis where Y is either a maximum or a minimum, i.e., those points on the real axis for which

$$\frac{dY}{dn} = 0$$

Y is the stationary phase at these points. This method was used by Lamb for an investigation of waves caused by ships; it actually dates back to Lord Kelvin.

An attempt could be made to extend this method to the case where the exponent has the form $X + iY$ instead of the pure imaginary iY. It seems that ϕe^X could be taken as one part, provided X is slowly varying, and the above procedures could be applied. However, X is no longer slowly varying if X and Y are the real and imaginary parts of the same function f. They are connected by the well known relations

$$\frac{\partial X}{\partial \xi} = \frac{\partial Y}{\partial \eta}, \qquad \frac{\partial X}{\partial \eta} = -\frac{\partial Y}{\partial \xi}$$

where

$$n = \xi + i\eta, \qquad f = X + iY$$

Thus, even if X is, in general, slowly varying along the real axis, still, just where the imaginary part is stationary, X varies rapidly. For a point on the real axis where $\partial Y/\partial \xi = 0$, an equipotential of Y must be tangent to the real axis. But, since equipotentials of Y (see Section 1) are lines of steepest descent of X, then at this point on the real axis, $\partial X/\partial \xi$ is large.

At the start of this investigation it was shown that by deforming the path of integration in the complex n plane, only the neighborhood of the saddle points had to be considered.

For the case $X = 0$ on the real axis, the points of stationary phase are saddle points. Then, one actually has

$$X = 0, \qquad \frac{\partial X}{\partial \xi} = 0, \qquad \text{i.e.,} \qquad \frac{\partial Y}{\partial \eta} = 0$$

and, as the condition for stationary phase, $\partial Y/\partial \xi = 0$. For this case, then, the methods of saddle points and of stationary phase agree.

If X is not zero, then, in general, a point of stationary phase is not a saddle point, and only one line of descent is tangent to the real axis. This is of no special interest; the saddle points will lie somewhere else but not upon the real axis.

As an example, it will be shown that in the case which was discussed here, the stationary phase method leads to results which are partly incorrect.

The integral

$$\frac{1}{2\pi}\,\mathrm{Re}\int_{+\infty}^{-\infty}\frac{e^{-i(nt-kx)}}{n-\nu}\,dn$$

has to be evaluated, and the real axis is now used as the path of integration. For real n, it is known that (see Eqs. 2 and 7′):

$$k=\frac{n}{c}\mu, \qquad \mu=\mu_r+i\mu_i$$

The phase is stationary for

$$t-\frac{dk_r}{dn}x=0, \qquad \Theta-\frac{d(n\mu_r)}{dn}=0$$

or

$$\Theta-\frac{c}{U}=0$$

where U is the group velocity, which is shown in Fig. 19 as a function of n. In the region of anomalous dispersion, this curve extends below 1 and even below zero. The points of stationary phase are given by the intersections of this curve with a line parallel to the axis at a value Θ. Thus points of stationary phase could exist for values of Θ less than 1 and even less than zero. The integration near these points would give a result different than zero, i.e., forerunners would exist which propagate with a velocity greater than that of light, which is impossible.

CHAPTER IV

PROPAGATION OF ELECTROMAGNETIC WAVES IN MATERIAL MEDIA*

1. Definitions: Role of a Dielectric Coefficient Depending on Density and Temperature

The discussion of Chapter III indicates a variety of circumstances in which the group velocity plays an important role. These results were obtained on a special example, but their significance appears to be very general. It is therefore appropriate to state the problem in general terms, without using a special model, and to see how much can be proved in this way. We shall see that all the most important results can be obtained, provided the absorption coefficient is small enough to be neglected.

Let us first recall the fundamental equations of electromagnetism in vacuum: calling $\boldsymbol{D}$ and $\boldsymbol{E}$ the displacement and electric field, $\boldsymbol{B}$ and $\boldsymbol{H}$ the induction field and magnetic intensity, ρ and $\boldsymbol{J}$ the charge density and electric current density, Maxwell's equations are written as

(1) $$\operatorname{curl} \boldsymbol{H} = 4\pi \boldsymbol{J} + \frac{\partial \boldsymbol{D}}{\partial t}, \qquad \operatorname{div} \boldsymbol{B} = 0$$

(2) $$\operatorname{curl} \boldsymbol{E} = -\frac{\partial \boldsymbol{B}}{\partial t}, \qquad \operatorname{div} \boldsymbol{D} = 4\pi\rho$$

(3) $$\boldsymbol{D} = \varepsilon_0 \boldsymbol{E}, \qquad \boldsymbol{B} = \mu_0 \boldsymbol{H}$$

ε_0 is the dielectric coefficient (or permittivity) and μ_0 the magnetic permeability of free space. These two coefficients have magnitudes

* Chapters IV and V were first published by L. Brillouin: "Congrès International d'Electricité, Paris, 1932," Vol. 2, pp. 739–788. Gauthier-Villars, Paris, 1933.

which depend on the chosen system of units, and are connected by the relation

$$\varepsilon_0 \mu_0 c^2 = 1 \tag{4}$$

c being the velocity of light in vacuum.

Since the coefficients ε_0 and μ_0 are constants, it is possible to define an energy density $\mathscr{E}$ given by

$$\mathscr{E} = \frac{\varepsilon_0}{8\pi} E^2 + \frac{\mu_0}{8\pi} H^2 \tag{5}$$

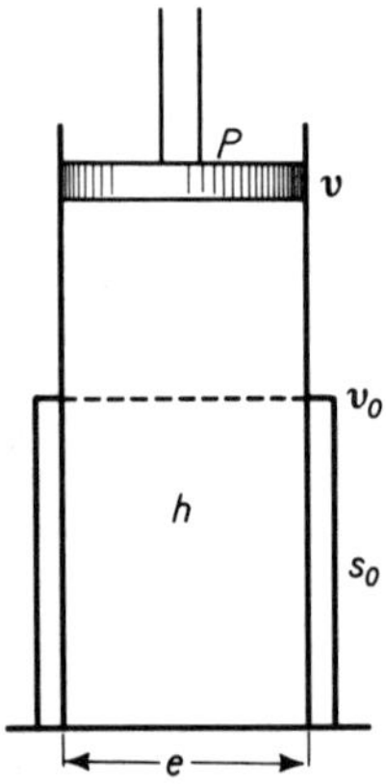

FIG. 1.

In general, these equations are written in the same form for a material medium, with the coefficients ε and μ being characteristic of the medium. This leads to the prediction that the velocity of propagation W for electromagnetic waves is given by

$$\varepsilon \mu W^2 = 1 \tag{6}$$

Experience shows that (even setting aside the phenomenon of hysteresis) the problem rapidly becomes more complicated. In Eqs. (3), the coefficients ε and μ in a material medium depend on temperature, on elastic deformations, and on frequency. In a fluid, ε and μ will still be functions of T, v (specific volume), and frequency.

It is appropriate now to recall briefly the role played, in thermodynamics and electrostatics, by a dielectric coefficient $\varepsilon(v,T)$. Assume a parallel capacitor of volume v_0 in which there exists a constant electric field E. The liquid fills this condenser and occupies a total volume $v > v_0$. The pressure p is *measured outside the condenser*. Simple thermodynamic considerations then lead to the following relations for the internal energy $U(v,T,E)$, the pressure $p(v,T,E)$, and the entropy S considered as a function of the same variables:

$$U(v,T,E) = U(v,T,0) + \frac{v_0 E^2}{8\pi}\left(\varepsilon + T\frac{\partial \varepsilon}{\partial T}\right) \tag{7a}$$

(7b) $$p(v,T,E) = p(v,T,0) + \frac{v_0 E^2}{8\pi}\frac{\partial \varepsilon}{\partial v}$$

(7c) $$S(v,T,E) = S(v,T,0) + \frac{v_0 E^2}{8\pi}\frac{\partial \varepsilon}{\partial T}$$

Comparing Eq. (7a) with Eq. (5) which is valid if ε is constant, it can be seen that upon charging a condenser (at constant volume) an amount of work $v_0(\varepsilon E^2/8\pi)$ must be done and an amount of heat $v_0(E^2/8\pi)T(\partial\varepsilon/\partial T)$ must be supplied. The increase in internal energy is the sum of these two.[1] Expression (8) represents the *free energy* (or Helmholtz thermodynamic potential):

(8) $$\Psi(v,T,E) = U - TS = \Psi(v,T,0) + v_0\frac{\varepsilon E^2}{8\pi}$$

---

[1] The electric charge on the plates is $q = s_0\varepsilon E/4\pi$ if s_0 is the area of the plates. For an infinitesimal change dv, dT, and dE, the work (mechanical and electrical) furnished by the system is

$$d\mathcal{T} = p\,dv - eE\,dq = \left[p - \frac{v_0E^2}{4\pi}\frac{\partial\varepsilon}{\partial v}\right]dv - \frac{v_0\varepsilon E}{4\pi}\,dE - \frac{v_0}{4\pi}E^2\frac{\partial\varepsilon}{\partial T}\,dT$$

if e is the distance between plates ($es_0 = v_0$). The internal energy $U(v,T,E)$ is increased by

$$dU = \frac{\partial U}{\partial v}\,dv + \frac{\partial U}{\partial E}\,dE + \frac{\partial U}{\partial T}\,dT$$

The heat dQ into the system is equal to $dU + d\mathcal{T}$ and the change in entropy dS is written as

$$dS = \frac{dQ}{T} = \frac{dU + d\mathcal{T}}{T} = \left[\frac{\partial U}{\partial v} + p - \frac{v_0E^2}{4\pi}\frac{\partial\varepsilon}{\partial v}\right]\frac{dv}{T} + \left[\frac{\partial U}{\partial E} - \frac{v_0\varepsilon E}{4\pi}\right]\frac{dE}{T} + \left[\frac{\partial U}{\partial T} - \frac{v_0E^2}{4\pi}\frac{\partial\varepsilon}{\partial T}\right]\frac{dT}{T}$$

Then, one uses the fact that dS is an exact differential. Considering p as a function of v, T, and E, one finally gets the relations

$$\frac{\partial U}{\partial E} = \frac{v_0E}{4\pi}\left(\varepsilon + T\frac{\partial\varepsilon}{\partial T}\right), \qquad \frac{\partial p}{\partial E} = \frac{v_0E}{4\pi}\frac{\partial\varepsilon}{\partial v}$$

which give the relations in Eq. (7).

Hence, the *electrical free energy density* η can be represented by a formula identical with Eq. (5), while the electrical energy density $\mathscr{E}_e$ is different, and contains a term in $T(\partial\varepsilon/\partial T)$ corresponding to heat exchange.

$$\text{(9)} \qquad \eta_e = \frac{\varepsilon E^2}{8\pi}$$

$$\mathscr{E}_e = \frac{E^2}{8\pi}\left(\varepsilon + T\frac{\partial\varepsilon}{\partial T}\right)$$

Formulas (7) also show that the electric field contributes to the pressure p. This contribution yields electrostriction. A field E applied to a liquid under constant pressure produces a contraction. Let δv be the change in the total volume:

$$\text{(10)} \qquad \delta v = -\left(\frac{\partial v}{\partial p}\right)\frac{v_0 E^2}{8\pi}\frac{\partial\varepsilon}{\partial v} = -\kappa v\frac{v_0 E^2}{8\pi}\frac{\partial\varepsilon}{\partial v} = -\frac{v_0 E^2}{8\pi}\left(\frac{\partial\varepsilon}{\partial p}\right)_{\substack{E=0\\ T=\text{constant}}}$$

where κ is the compressibility. This last formula is known as the law of Helmholtz-Lippman. These effects are usually very small except in some special chemicals, and we shall ignore them.

2. Dependence of the Dielectric Coefficient on Frequency; Evaluation of the Electrical Energy

For rapid electrical oscillations, no exchange of heat can practically occur, and the phenomena occur adiabatically. Keeping the volume constant and negligible electrostriction results in a simplification of the formulas, and the energy density takes the effective value of

$$\text{(11)} \qquad (\mathscr{E}_e)_{\text{adiabatic}} = \frac{\varepsilon E^2}{8\pi}$$

The complications envisaged in the preceeding paragraphs therefore disappear for electrical oscillations of high frequency, and in particular for electromagnetic waves.

It is still necessary to cope with the difficulties arising from the fact that the dielectric coefficient ε depends greatly on the frequency.

The permeability μ causes no difficulty, since it differs only very slightly from μ_0 for all the usual transparent media.

Since ε depends on frequency, it becomes very difficult to define an electrical energy. Even if the value of the electric field E is known at an instant t, still, the energy stored is completely unknown. It is necessary to know how the field was established. If the field was established by a slow and continuous variation, Eq. (11) can be used, in which ε is the dielectric coefficient appropriate for very low frequencies. If the field E reaches its value after a succession of oscillations, all their frequencies must be known. If these frequencies cannot be defined even approximately, it becomes impossible to evaluate the energy!

These ideas will now be illustrated by an example. Consider a plane capacitor of unit volume containing a field E. Then the surface charge density on the plates will be $D/4\pi$. If E and D are changed, the work done by the electrical forces is

$$\mathscr{T}_e = \frac{1}{4\pi}\int_{D_0}^{D_1} E\,dD = \mathscr{E}_1 - \mathscr{E}_0 \tag{12}$$

assuming an adiabatic situation and calling $\mathscr{E}_0$ and $\mathscr{E}_1$ the initial and final energies, respectively. Consider now an oscillating field E and a correspondingly varying D.

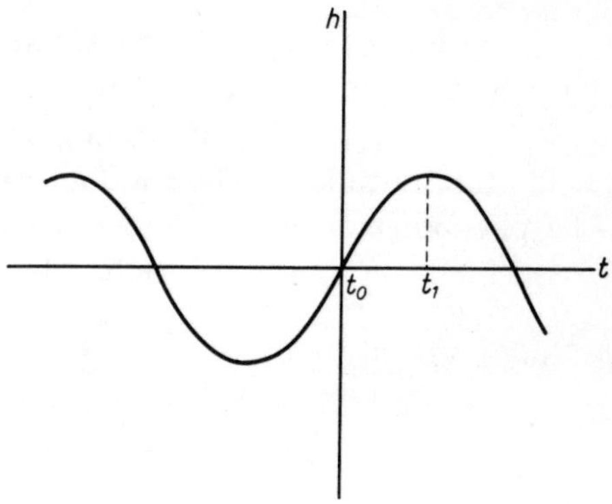

FIG. 2.

$$E = a \sin \omega t,$$

$$D = \varepsilon(\omega) a \sin \omega t$$

It is simple to evaluate the difference between the energy at time $t = 0$ when the field is zero and at time $t = \pi/2\omega$ when the field has its maximum value a, and

$$\mathscr{E}_1 - \mathscr{E}_0 = \frac{\varepsilon(\omega)}{8\pi} a^2 \tag{13}$$

Does this represent the total energy when $E = a$? Certainly not. The energy $\mathscr{E}_0$ at the time when E passes through zero is quite different from the zero energy that the dielectric has after being isolated from an electric field for a long time. In order to explain the fact that the permittivity ε of the dielectric is different from that of the vacuum, ε_0, one must admit that the medium contains mobile charges, electrons or ions in motion or electric dipoles capable of orientation; then, one takes as the zero energy of the system the condition that all of the charged particles are at rest in their equilibrium positions. In the previous example, all the charged particles may pass by their equilibrium positions at the time $t = 0$ when the field vanishes, but they pass them with nonzero velocity. In formula (13), the energy $\mathscr{E}_0$ represents the *kinetic energy of all the charged particles* contained in the dielectric. The average energy during the oscillations is

$$\bar{\mathscr{E}}_a = \mathscr{E}_0 + \frac{\varepsilon}{8\pi}\frac{a^2}{2} \tag{14}$$

In order to obtain the total value of the energy in an oscillating electric field, it is necessary to consider a process which, starting at rest ($E = 0$ for a certain time), slowly builds up to an oscillating field of amplitude a. The total energy can be obtained by considering the phenomenon of slow beats between two oscillating fields having frequencies ω' and ω'' only slightly different, $\omega' = \omega + \nu$ and $\omega'' = \omega - \nu$.

$$\begin{aligned} E &= \frac{a}{2}(\cos \omega' t - \cos \omega'' t) = -a \sin \nu t \sin \omega t \\ D &= \frac{a}{2}(\varepsilon' \cos \omega' t - \varepsilon'' \cos \omega'' t) \\ \frac{dD}{dt} &= -\frac{a}{2}(\varepsilon'\omega' \sin \omega' t - \varepsilon''\omega'' \sin \omega'' t) \\ &= -a\left(\varepsilon\omega \sin \nu t \cos \omega t + \nu \frac{\partial(\varepsilon\omega)}{\partial\omega} \cos \nu t \sin \omega t\right) \end{aligned} \tag{15}$$

This last formula is obtained by expanding $\sin \omega' t$ and $\sin \omega'' t$, and writing

$$(16) \qquad \begin{aligned} \varepsilon' \omega' &= \varepsilon\omega + \nu \frac{\partial(\varepsilon\omega)}{\partial\omega} \cdots \\ \varepsilon'' \omega'' &= \varepsilon\omega - \nu \frac{\partial(\varepsilon\omega)}{\partial\omega} \cdots \end{aligned}$$

This calculation rests on the assumption that the approximations (16) are sufficient, which requires that the dielectric coefficient $\mathscr{E}$ *must not vary too quickly* as a function of frequency, and *must always remain real* (no losses, no hysteresis).

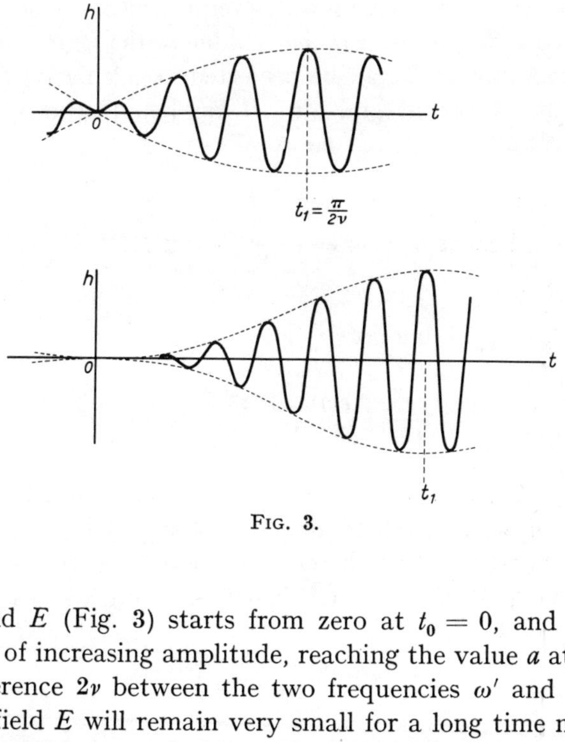

FIG. 3.

The field E (Fig. 3) starts from zero at $t_0 = 0$, and consists of oscillations of increasing amplitude, reaching the value a at $t_1 = \pi/2\nu$. If the difference 2ν between the two frequencies ω' and ω'' is very small, the field E will remain very small for a long time near $t_0 = 0$, and the establishment of the oscillations will require a long time. Evaluating the energy gained during the time $t_1 - t_0$ we get,

$$\mathscr{E} = \frac{1}{4\pi} \int_0^{t_1} E\, dD = \frac{\varepsilon a^2}{4\pi} \omega \int_0^{t_1} \sin^2 \nu t \cos \omega t \sin \omega t\, dt$$

$$+ \frac{a^2}{4\pi} \nu \frac{\partial(\varepsilon\omega)}{\partial\omega} \int_0^{t_1} \sin^2 \omega t \cos \nu t \sin \nu t\, dt$$

The terms in $\cos \nu t$ or $\sin \nu t$ are slowly varying. Those with $\cos \omega t$ or $\sin \omega t$ vary very rapidly. The first integral

$$\frac{1}{2} \int \sin^2 \nu t \sin 2\omega t\, dt$$

averages to zero. It contributes a term which oscillates between $\pm\ 1/8\omega$, since at t_1 the instantaneous value of the field is $+\ a$ or $-\ a$. Therefore, this first term can be neglected in calculating the average energy. In the second integral $\sin^2 \omega t$ can be replaced by its average value 1/2 and the term rewritten as

$$\frac{1}{2} \int_0^{\pi/2\nu} \cos \nu t \sin \nu t\, dt = -\frac{1}{8\nu} [\cos 2\nu t]_0^{\pi/2\nu} = \frac{1}{4\nu}$$

The final result is therefore

$$\bar{\mathscr{E}} = \frac{a^2}{16\pi} \frac{\partial(\varepsilon\omega)}{\partial\omega} = \frac{a^2}{16\pi} \left(\varepsilon + \omega \frac{\partial\varepsilon}{\partial\omega}\right) \tag{17}$$

A more exact calculation of the integrals gives the same result. A comparison of formulas (14) and (17) shows that at the moment when the field passes through zero (during a series of regular oscillations), the energy of the dielectric is not zero, but rather it is equal to

$$\mathscr{E}_0 = \frac{a^2}{16\pi} \omega \frac{\partial\varepsilon}{\partial\omega} \tag{17'}$$

This term represents the kinetic energy of the charge carriers in the dielectric.

The preceding results are independent of the particular manner in which the amplitude varies. The same result ensues for any manner of variation as long as the variation is sufficiently slow. For example, the variation shown in the second part of Fig. 3 given by

$$E = \frac{a}{2}(\cos \omega' t + \cos \omega'' t) - a \cos \omega t = a \cos \omega t\,(\cos \nu t - 1)$$

is easily analyzed in the same manner. The minimum in the field at $t = 0$ is more prolonged than that for the variation of E given in Eq. (15), and the maximum occurs at $t_1 = \pi/\nu$.

3. Waves; Phase Velocity; Energy Density of a Plane Wave

It is easy to see that Maxwell's equations (1), (2), (3), written with the coefficients ε and μ, predict a velocity W, defined by Eq. (6), for a plane monochromatic wave.

Consider a polarized wave propagating in the x direction and given by

(18) $$H_y = A \cos \omega\left(t - \frac{x}{W}\right), \qquad E_z = a \cos \omega\left(t - \frac{x}{W}\right)$$

It is easy to obtain from these relationships, inserted into Maxwell's equations, the relations

(19) $$\varepsilon\mu W^2 = 1, \qquad \varepsilon a^2 = \frac{aA}{W} = \mu A^2$$

What is the average energy density in the region traversed by this plane wave? It is not difficult to find the magnetic energy, and the electrical energy is given by Eq. (17). Thus,

(20) $$\begin{aligned} \mathscr{E} &= \frac{1}{16\pi}\left(a^2\varepsilon + a^2\omega\frac{\partial\varepsilon}{\partial\omega} + \mu A^2\right) \\ &= \frac{a^2}{8\pi}\left(\varepsilon + \frac{1}{2}\,\omega\,\frac{\partial\varepsilon}{\partial\omega}\right) = \frac{\varepsilon_1 a^2}{8\pi} \end{aligned}$$

making use of the relations (19). Thus, the energy is proportional to the intensity a^2 of the wave, times a new *coefficient* ε_1 *which is different from the dielectric coefficient*:

$$\varepsilon_1 = \varepsilon + \frac{1}{2}\,\omega\,\frac{\partial \varepsilon}{\partial \omega} \tag{20'}$$

This value for ε_1 is evidently only the beginning of an expansion, and this abbreviated expression cannot be used unless ε varies slowly with ω, a condition which is necessary for the validity of the calculation in the preceeding sections. It is just as necessary that ε *must be real*; in other words there can be no absorption of the wave (neither losses, nor hysteresis).

The velocity W which was just discussed is the *phase velocity*. Formulas (18) give its precise meaning. This velocity W enables one to calculate the phase difference between two points x_1 and x_2. It enters in all phenomena involving interference and stationary waves. It serves to define the wavelength of the wave

$$\lambda = W\tau = \frac{2\pi W}{\omega}$$

and also is used in the definition of the *index of refraction* n,

$$n = \frac{c}{W} = \sqrt{\frac{\varepsilon\mu}{\varepsilon_0\mu_0}} \tag{21}$$

and enters into the laws of refraction at the interface between two bodies.

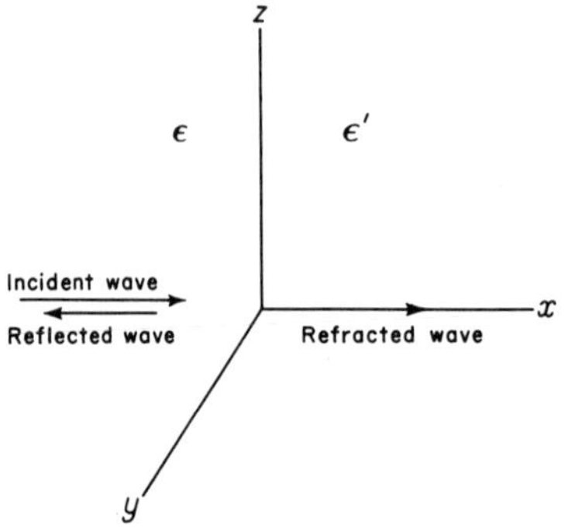

FIG. 4.

The laws of refraction follow from the boundary conditions for electric and magnetic fields at the interface of the media. The tangential components of E and H and the normal components of D and B must be continuous.

Consider the following example: A wave is incident normally on a plane surface separating two media of dielectric powers ε and ε'; assume that $\mu = \mu'$. The various waves are then:

Incident	$E_z = a \cos\omega\left(t - \frac{x}{W}\right)$	$H_y = A \cos\omega\left(t - \frac{x}{W}\right)$
Refracted	$E_z = a' \cos\omega\left(t - \frac{x}{W'}\right)$	$H_y = A' \cos\omega\left(t - \frac{x}{W'}\right)$
Reflected	$E_z = a'' \cos\omega\left(t + \frac{x}{W}\right)$	$H_y = -A'' \cos\omega\left(t + \frac{x}{W}\right)$

The normal components are zero. The conditions of continuity for the tangential components (for $x = 0$) give

(22) $$a + a'' = a', \qquad A - A'' = A'$$

Using the relations (19), the second condition can be written

(22a) $$\sqrt{\frac{\varepsilon}{\mu}}(a - a'') = \sqrt{\frac{\varepsilon'}{\mu'}}\,a'$$

but

$$\sqrt{\frac{\varepsilon}{\mu}} = \varepsilon W \qquad \text{and} \qquad \sqrt{\frac{\varepsilon'}{\mu'}} = \varepsilon' W'$$

Multiplying the two conditions (22) and (22a) together gives

(22b) $$\varepsilon W(a^2 - a''^2) = \varepsilon' W' a'^2$$

This relation will be very useful later on. *It is valid even if the permittivities of the dielectrics ε and ε' are functions of the frequency.* In case ε and ε' are independent of frequency, this relation has a clear physical meaning: the velocities W and W' are independent of frequency and represent the velocity with which energy is transported in the wave. (The following Section will show that this is no longer true if W depends on frequency.)

The energy transported across a unit surface perpendicular to the direction of propagation during one second is thus

$$\mathscr{E}W = \frac{\varepsilon a^2}{8\pi} W$$

since in Eq. (20) there is no difference between ε and ε_1. Formula (22b) thus simply expresses the fact that the incident energy is equal to the sum of the reflected and refracted energy.

4. The Group Velocity U

In a medium in which all waves have the same velocity of propagation (such as vacuum for electromagnetic waves) a signal of any form at all will propagate without deformation. The form of the wave plays no part in the propagation. The velocity of propagation can be defined as the phase velocity, since it also represents the velocity with which the energy or any other quantity is transported.

In a dispersive medium, the situation is otherwise. All propagation is accompanied by a change in the form of the signal, except for an infinitely long sinusoidal wave. In one word — if there is dispersion, there is also distortion. The example of propagation of electrical perturbations along cables is well known.

In attempting to define a velocity of energy transport, several different possibilities exist. It is the intention of this paper to examine several of these, and to show that they are, in general, consistent with each other.

First, consider the *group velocity*. When an infinite sinusoidal wave

$$E = a \cos(\omega t - ax - by - cz)$$

(23)

$$a^2 + b^2 + c^2 = \frac{4\pi^2}{\lambda^2} = \frac{\omega^2}{W^2}$$

travels through a medium, there is a uniform average energy density throughout the space, given by Eq. (17). Does this energy remain where it is, or does it propagate through the medium? It is impossible to know this. In order to observe a propagation of energy, it is necessary to suppose that an excess of energy [in comparison with the uniform energy of the wave described by Eq. (23)] exists at a certain time at some point in space, and then to ascertain whether this energy moves with time.

The simplest definition is obtained by assuming that initially there exists a small excess of energy regularly distributed throughout the space, as if it resulted from the superposition of two plane waves with only slightly different frequencies and/or directions of propagation. These two waves produce *beats* and the propagation of these beats will be observed.

Assume two closely similar waves

$$E' = a \cos(\omega' t - a' x - b' y - c' z)$$
$$E'' = a \cos(\omega'' t - a'' x - b'' y - c'' z)$$

with

$$(24) \qquad \begin{aligned} \omega' &= \omega + \nu, & a' &= a + \alpha, & b' &= b + \beta, & c' &= c + \gamma \\ \omega'' &= \omega - \nu, & a'' &= a - \alpha, & b'' &= b - \beta, & c'' &= c - \gamma \end{aligned}$$

The result of superposing these two waves is

$$E' + E'' = 2a \cos(\nu t - \alpha x - \beta y - \gamma z) \cos(\omega t - ax - by - cz)$$

which can be described as a plane wave of frequency ω and wavelength λ, where

$$(25) \qquad \frac{2\pi}{\lambda} = \sqrt{a^2 + b^2 + c^2}$$

The wave's amplitude varies with beats of frequency ν and a law of propagation given by

$$\cos(\nu t - \alpha x - \beta y - \gamma z)$$

This defines a wavelength Λ of the beats and a velocity of propagation U

$$(26) \qquad \frac{2\pi}{\Lambda} = \sqrt{\alpha^2 + \beta^2 + \gamma^2}, \qquad U = \frac{\Lambda \nu}{2\pi} = \frac{\nu}{\sqrt{\alpha^2 + \beta^2 + \gamma^2}}$$

This velocity U can be zero, if the two interfering waves have the same frequency, i.e., if ν is zero (stationary waves). The velocity U has its maximum value when the beats are produced by two waves having the same direction of propagation and only slightly different frequencies. This requires setting

$$\alpha = \zeta a, \qquad \beta = \zeta b, \qquad \gamma = \zeta c \qquad (\nu \text{ and } \zeta \text{ very small})$$

The values $a + \alpha$, $b + \beta$, $c + \gamma$, and $\omega + \nu$, used with the conventions of Eq. (24), require that the wave E' have a wavelength λ' such that

$$\frac{2\pi}{\lambda'} = \sqrt{a'^2 + b'^2 + c'^2} = \sqrt{a^2 + b^2 + c^2}\,(1 + \zeta) = \frac{2\pi}{\lambda}(1 + \zeta)$$

using Eq. (25). Therefore,

$$\frac{\zeta}{\lambda} = \frac{1}{\lambda'} - \frac{1}{\lambda} = \nu \frac{\partial(1/\lambda)}{\partial\omega}$$

when the two wavelengths λ' and λ differ only slightly. The velocity of propagation of these beats is therefore

$$U = \frac{\nu}{\sqrt{\alpha^2 + \beta^2 + \gamma^2}} = \frac{\nu\lambda}{2\pi\zeta} = \frac{1}{2\pi}\frac{\partial(\omega)}{\partial(1/\lambda)}$$

which can also be written as

$$\frac{1}{U} = \frac{\partial(\omega/W)}{\partial\omega} = \frac{\partial k}{\partial\omega} \tag{27}$$

where $k = (2\pi/\lambda) = (\omega/W)$.

This maximum velocity of propagation of beats is called *the group velocity* U.

These calculations, as well as the preceding ones, neglect the effects of absorption.

5. Velocity of Energy Transport U_1

Consider a homogeneous medium through which an infinite sinusoidal wave [Eq. (18)] is propagating. The value of the average energy density has been defined in Eq. (20) as

$$\mathscr{E} = \frac{\varepsilon_1 a^2}{8\pi} \qquad \left(\varepsilon_1 = \varepsilon + \frac{\omega}{2}\frac{\partial\varepsilon}{\partial\omega}\right) \tag{20}$$

If this energy propagates with a velocity U_1, then in this medium there will be an energy flux density

$$I = U_1\mathscr{E} = \varepsilon_1 U_1 \frac{a^2}{8\pi} \tag{28}$$

This is, by definition, the energy passing per second through a surface of unit area perpendicular to the direction of propagation. Can this energy flux actually be calculated? Yes, by proceeding as in Section 3 [Fig. 4, Eq. (22)]. Consider a plane $x = 0$ bounding the medium under study, and inquire as to what incident wave a falling on this surface $x = 0$ produces a refracted wave a', which is just the one being considered, inside the medium. There will also be a reflected wave a'', and it has been shown that the condition of refraction gives the relationship

$$\varepsilon W[a^2 - (a'')^2] = \varepsilon' W' a'^2 \tag{22b}$$

Using the condition that the energy flux in the refracted wave is equal to the difference in the energy flux of the incident and reflected wave, one finds that

$$\varepsilon_1 U_1 [a^2 - (a'')^2] = \varepsilon_1' U_1' a'^2 \tag{29}$$

using the definitions for terms in Eq. (28). These two conditions, (28) and (29), are valid if the first medium is a vacuum and

$$\varepsilon = \varepsilon_1 = 1, \qquad W = U_1 = c$$

which leads to the curious relation

$$\varepsilon' W' = \varepsilon_1' U_1' \tag{30}$$

The primes in these formulas can be removed from now on. It is easy to see that this *velocity of energy transport* is equal to the group velocity when the approximations made in Sections 2, 3, and 4 are fulfilled, i.e., when ε is a slowly varying function of the frequency ω.

Condition (30) states, in effect, that

$$\frac{1}{U_1} = \frac{\varepsilon_1}{\varepsilon W} = \frac{1}{W}\left(1 + \frac{\omega}{2\varepsilon}\frac{\partial \varepsilon}{\partial \omega}\right) = \frac{1}{W}\left(1 + \omega \frac{\partial \log \sqrt{\varepsilon}}{\partial \omega}\right) \tag{31}$$

while the group velocity is, after Eq. (27),

$$\frac{1}{U} = \frac{\partial(\omega/W)}{\partial \omega} = \frac{1}{W}\left(1 - \frac{\omega}{W}\frac{\partial W}{\partial \omega}\right) = \frac{1}{W}\left(1 - \omega \frac{\partial \log W}{\partial \omega}\right) \tag{31'}$$

which is the same, as that given in Eq. (31), since

$$W = \frac{1}{\sqrt{\varepsilon\mu}}$$

This agreement loses its validity only in regions where ε varies rapidly with ω, or if there is absorption.

6. Signal Velocity, S

The problem of energy transport can be attacked differently, by ascertaining how a well-defined signal propagates in a material medium. Suppose that at the point $x = 0$ a light wave is emitted with a period τ, but only for a limited time T; the problem is to investigate the character of the wave at a distance x from the point of emission. The resultant wave will be greatly deformed. Immediately after the signal front some very weak oscillations or "forerunners" will arrive. Then, at a certain moment, the amplitude of the signal will take on large values, which will signify clearly the arrival of the signal. In many cases, it is possible to determine the exact moment when the main signal arrives, which defines the *signal velocity*.

In general, the signal velocity measured depends on the sensitivity of the detecting apparatus used. With a very sensitive detector, even the forerunners, or certain parts of them, might be detected, and the resulting measurement would imply a very large velocity of propagation. But if the sensitivity of the detector is restricted to a quarter or half the final signal intensity, then an unambiguous definition of the signal velocity can, in general, be given.

Instead of considering the advent of the signal, it is possible to consider the end of the signal. Evidently, the same result will ensue since a signal terminated at both ends can be considered as composed of two signals, one terminated in front (starting at $t = 0$ and continuing indefinitely) and another similar signal of opposite sign beginning at $t = T$ and continuing indefinitely. The end of the signal is therefore characterized by the same features as the wave front, with signs of forerunners, and an equally well-defined end corresponding to a velocity S.

The mathematical methods used here are a bit complicated. The signal is represented by a Fourier integral, i.e., by a sum of infinitely long oscillations. For each term of this sum, there is a known law of propagation with a phase velocity corresponding to its frequency. The form of the wave after travelling a distance x is then given by another Fourier integral which must then be evaluated. The main difficulty lies in this resumming of the component oscillations after each of them has travelled through this distance x and undergone different change of phase.

The Fourier analysis of the signal represented by Fig. 5, i.e., the function

$$f(t) = \begin{cases} 0 & (t < 0) \\ \sin \omega_0 t & (0 < t < T) \\ 0 & (T < t) \end{cases} \tag{32}$$

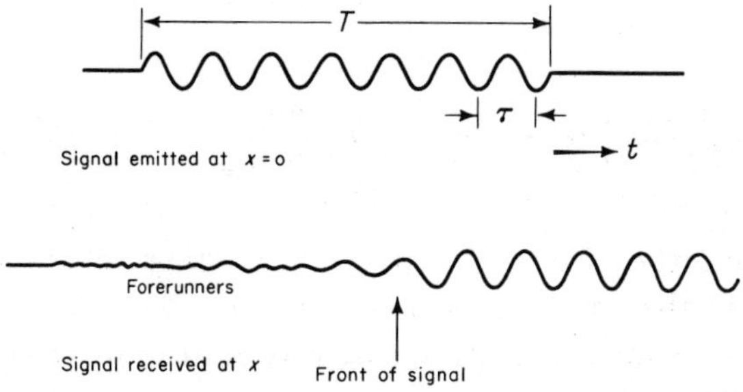

FIG. 5.

with

$$T = N\tau = \frac{2N\pi}{\omega_0}$$

proceeds as follows. The well known relations

$$f(t) = \int_0^\infty (C_\omega \cos \omega t + S_\omega \sin \omega t)\, d\omega$$

$$C_\omega = \frac{1}{\pi} \int_{-\infty}^{\infty} f(\alpha) \cos \omega\alpha \, d\alpha \tag{33}$$

$$S_\omega = \frac{1}{\pi} \int_{-\infty}^{\infty} f(\alpha) \sin \omega\alpha \, d\alpha$$

are used. For the function f, the two integrals C_ω and S_ω reduce to integrals between 0 and T and are easily evaluated. After several simple transformations, they yield:

$$(34)\quad f(t) = \frac{1}{2\pi}\int_0^\infty \left(\frac{1}{\omega - \omega_0} - \frac{1}{\omega + \omega_0}\right)[\cos \omega(t - T) - \cos \omega t]\, d\omega$$

$$= \frac{2\omega_0}{\pi}\int_0^\infty \sin \frac{\omega T}{2} \sin \omega \left(t - \frac{T}{2}\right)\frac{d\omega}{\omega^2 - {\omega_0}^2}$$

$$= \frac{1}{2\pi}\int_{-\infty}^{+\infty} [\cos \omega(t - T) - \cos \omega t]\frac{d\omega}{\omega - \omega_0}$$

$$= \frac{1}{2\pi}\,\mathrm{Re}\int_{-\infty}^{+\infty} (e^{i\omega(t-T)} - e^{i\omega t})\frac{d\omega}{\omega - \omega_0}$$

Depending on the situation, one or the other of these equivalent expressions is the most convenient one to use. The signal is thus analyzed into a sum of infinitely long waves. The wave of frequency ω has an intensity of

$$(35)\qquad J = \left(\frac{2\omega_0}{\pi}\frac{\sin\frac{\omega T}{2}}{\omega^2 - {\omega_0}^2}\right)^2, \qquad T = \frac{2N\pi}{\omega_0}$$

[See Eq. (34), second form.]

This expression has a very high maximum for $\omega = \omega_0$, which is not infinite because the sine in the numerator becomes zero at the same time as the denominator. This maximum is

$$J_{\max} = \left(\frac{N}{\omega_0}\right)^2$$

Figure 6 is a graph of expression (35) and is similar to Figs. 3 and 4 of Chapter II. The curves 1, 2, and 3 of the second figure show how the envelope of the curve reacts to an increase in the time $T = N\tau$

of the signal. The spectrum actually extends through all frequencies, from zero to infinity, but it has a well defined maximum at $\omega = \omega_0$. If only a band of frequencies around ω_0 is retained while the other frequencies are suppressed, the form of the signal is not greatly changed, but the front and the end of the signal lose their definiteness and become slightly blurred.

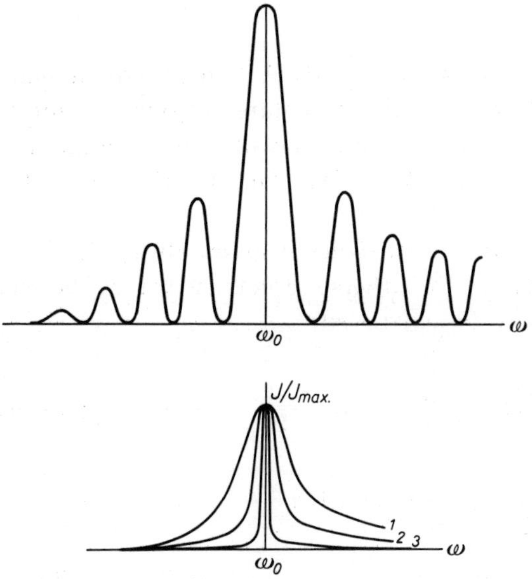

FIG. 6.

The first, third, and fourth forms of Eq. (34) separate into terms in $\cos \omega t$ and in $\cos \omega(t - T)$. The $\cos \omega t$ terms, if they are separated, give a sinusoidal signal beginning at $t = 0$ and lasting indefinitely thereafter, while the $\cos \omega(t - T)$ terms correspond to a similar signal (but with opposite sign) beginning at $t = T$ and cancelling the first signal at all later times.

It is tempting to separate these groups of terms. The unfortunate thing, however, is that a pole then appears for $\omega = \omega_0$ and the integral cannot retain its real form. It is necessary to use a path of integration in the complex ω plane which goes around this pole. This method was used in Chapters II and III but its mathematical complications will not be introduced here.

What happens to the signal after it traverses a distance x? Each wave ω propagates with its phase velocity $W(\omega)$ and the integral (34) becomes

$$(36)\qquad f(x,t) = \frac{1}{2\pi}\,\mathrm{Re}\int_{-\infty}^{+\infty}\left\{e^{i\omega\left(t-T-\frac{x}{W}\right)} - e^{i\omega\left(t-\frac{x}{W}\right)}\right\}\frac{d\omega}{\omega-\omega_0}$$

This integral must be evaluated. A complete discussion of the process was given in Chapter III; it requires recourse to integrations in the complex plane. The discussion will now be limited to the case of *propagation without absorption,* i.e., to the case of W remaining always real.[2]

The waves with frequencies near ω_0 always have a much greater amplitude than all the others. For these waves the second exponent in Eq. (36) may be expanded:

$$\omega\left(t-\frac{x}{W}\right) = \omega_0\left(t-\frac{x}{W_0}\right) + \left(t-\frac{x}{U_0}\right)(\omega-\omega_0)$$

$$\frac{1}{U} = \partial(\omega/W)/\partial\omega$$

The first exponent may be expanded similarly. This contributes

$$(37)\qquad \frac{1}{2\pi}\,\mathrm{Re}\, e^{i\omega_0\left(t-\frac{x}{W_0}\right)}\int_{\omega_0-\eta}^{\omega_0+\eta}\left[e^{i(\omega-\omega_0)\left(t-T-\frac{x}{U_0}\right)} - e^{i(\omega-\omega_0)\left(t-\frac{x}{U_0}\right)}\right]\frac{d\omega}{\omega-\omega_0}$$

---

[2] If there is absorption, with a coefficient κ, then a wave $e^{i\omega t}$ becomes, after traversing a distance x,

$$e^{-\kappa x}e^{i\omega\left(t-\frac{x}{W}\right)} = e^{i\omega\left(t-\frac{x}{W}+i\frac{\kappa x}{\omega}\right)}$$

which results in the definition of a complex velocity of propagation

$$\frac{1}{W_i} = \frac{1}{W} - i\frac{\kappa}{\omega}$$

which can be compared to the integral (34) written in an analogous form

$$(37') \qquad f(t) = \frac{1}{2\pi} \operatorname{Re} e^{i\omega_0 t} \int_{\omega_0 - \eta}^{\omega_0 + \eta} [e^{i(\omega - \omega_0)(t - T)} - e^{i(\omega - \omega_0)t}] \frac{d\omega}{\omega - \omega_0}$$

The integral (37′) is just Eq. (34) with the suppression of the frequencies very different from ω_0 in (34). It presents a signal beginning progressively at $t = 0$ and ending at $t = T$, while Eq. (34) yields a signal with a sudden start and a sudden end. The analogous integral (37) represents the same signal beginning gradually at $t = (x/U_0)$ and ending gradually at $t = T + (x/U_0)$. The principal part of the signal thus arrives at a depth x with a noticeable amplitude at about the time $t = (x/U_0)$ and ends at $T + (x/U_0)$. The front and end of the signal propagate with the *group velocity* U_0. But, at the same time, the *signal has been distorted*; the front and end of the signal are continuous rather than discontinuous as it was previously (cf. Fig. 5).

With these approximations, the velocity S of the wave-front is equal to the group velocity.

$$(38) \qquad S = U(\omega_0)$$

It is to be noted that there is an exponential factor in (37) with argument $i\omega[t - (x/W_0)]$, which shows that in the midst of the signal, the phase of the oscillations are determined by the phase velocity W.

7. The Forerunners

The forerunners mentioned earlier will now be investigated. After eliminating the frequencies near ω_0, we still have two integrals of the form

$$\frac{1}{2\pi} \operatorname{Re} \int A(\omega) e^{i\phi} \, d\omega$$

in Eq. (36), where the amplitude

$$A(\omega) = \frac{1}{\omega - \omega_0}$$

varies slowly and where the phase is ϕ. If the phase varies rapidly with ω, the integral is negligibly small. The amplitude A, multiplied by a periodic function of short period, makes a very small contribution to the integral. However, an appreciable contribution comes from those frequencies near which ϕ passes through a maximum[3] or a minimum,

$$\frac{\partial \phi}{\partial \omega} = 0 \tag{39}$$

If ω_1 is one root of Eq. (39), then $-\omega_1$ is another root, since it has been shown that $\pm\,\omega$ have the same phase velocity W.

First, the integral around ω_1 will be calculated, and then the integral around $-\omega_1$ will be added to this. ϕ can be expanded about ω_1 in a Taylor series, and the linear term will disappear by virtue of Eq. (39):

$$\phi = \phi_1 + \frac{(\omega - \omega_1)^2}{2}\left(\frac{\partial^2 \phi}{\partial \omega^2}\right)_{\omega = \omega_1} + \cdots$$

$$\begin{aligned} \phi_1 &= \omega_1 \left[t - \frac{x}{W(\omega_1)}\right], \\ \left(\frac{\partial \phi}{\partial \omega}\right)_1 &= t - \frac{x}{U(\omega_1)} = 0 \\ \left(\frac{\partial^2 \phi}{\partial \omega^2}\right)_1 &= -x \left(\frac{\partial \dfrac{1}{U}}{\partial \omega}\right)_1 \end{aligned} \tag{40}$$

Only values of ω near ω_1 play a noticeable part. Since A varies slowly, it can be taken in front of the integral sign, and the integral can then be written as

$$\frac{1}{2\pi}\,\mathrm{Re}\, A(\omega_1) \int e^{i\phi}\, d\omega$$

$$= \frac{1}{2\pi(\omega_1 - \omega_0)} \mathrm{Re} \exp\left\{i\omega_1\left(t - \frac{x}{W_1}\right)\right\} \int \exp\left\{-i(\omega - \omega_1)^2 \frac{x}{2} \frac{\partial(1/U)}{\partial \omega}\right\} d\omega$$

---

[3] This method of integration is called the "method of stationary phase"; its limits of application were discussed in Chapter III, Section 8.

Since only an approximate answer is necessary, the integral can be extended over the range $-\infty$ to $+\infty$ and becomes a Fresnel type

$$\int_{-\infty}^{+\infty} e^{i\xi^2}\,d\xi = \sqrt{\frac{\pi}{2}}\,(1+i) = \sqrt{\pi}\,e^{i(\pi/4)}$$

Thus, the integration near ω_1 results in

$$\frac{\sqrt{\pi}}{2\pi(\omega_1-\omega_0)}\,\mathrm{Re}\sqrt{\frac{2}{-x\,\dfrac{\partial(1/U)}{\partial\omega}}}\;e^{i\omega_1\left(t-\frac{x}{W_1}\right)+i\frac{\pi}{4}}$$

Assuming that $\partial(1/U)/\partial\omega$ is negative, the above is rewritten as

$$\frac{\cos\{\omega_1\,[t-(x/W_1)]+(\pi/4)\}}{(\omega_1-\omega_0)\sqrt{-2\pi x\,\dfrac{\partial(1/U)}{\partial\omega}}}$$

In case $\partial(1/U)/\partial\omega$ is positive, the expression is changed only by a reversal of the sign and by a change of $+(\pi/4)$ to $-(\pi/4)$. In effect, by changing the negative sign of the radical, a factor $i = -e^{-i(\pi/2)}$ is added, which modifies the real part of the expression.

To this result must be added the integral for $-\omega_1$. The second integral has the same cosine factor, but a factor of $-1/(\omega_1+\omega_0)$ instead of $1/(\omega_1+\omega_0)$. The sum of these two is

$$\frac{2\omega_0}{\omega_1{}^2-\omega_0{}^2}\;\frac{\cos\omega_1\left(t-\dfrac{x}{W_1}+\dfrac{\pi}{4}\right)}{\sqrt{-2\pi x\,\dfrac{\partial(1/U)}{\partial\omega}}} \tag{41}$$

At time t preceding the arrival of the principal part of the signal, the forerunners arrive at a point x with a velocity given by their group velocity [Eq. (40)]. These forerunners have a very small amplitude [Eq. (41)], except when the *group velocity is a maximum or a minimum.*

In the latter case, formula (41) gives an infinite amplitude! This merely shows that the approximations used up to this point are no longer valid. Since the second derivative of ϕ is zero, the expansion must be carried to the third term. Let ω_L be the frequency and t_L the time at which this anomaly occurs. This time is called the "quasi-latent time" by some authors.

$$
\text{(42)}\qquad
\begin{aligned}
&\omega_L \qquad \text{is defined by} \qquad \left[\frac{\partial(1/U)}{\partial\omega}\right]_{\omega_L} = 0 \\
&t_L \qquad \text{is defined by} \qquad t_L - \frac{x}{U(\omega_L)} = 0
\end{aligned}
$$

The forerunners at times

$$t = t_L + T' \qquad (T' \text{ small,}$$

will now be sought.

ϕ can be expanded near t_1 and ω_1 by writing

$$\phi(t,\omega) = \phi(t,\omega_L) + (\omega - \omega_L)\left(\frac{\partial\phi}{\partial\omega}\right)_{t,\omega_L} + \frac{(\omega-\omega_L)^2}{2}\left(\frac{\partial^2\phi}{\partial\omega^2}\right)_{t,\omega_L} + \frac{(\omega-\omega_L)^3}{6}\left(\frac{\partial^3\phi}{\partial\omega^3}\right)_{t,\omega_L} + \cdots$$

$$= \omega_L\left(t - \frac{x}{W_L}\right) + (\omega-\omega_L)T' - x\,\frac{(\omega-\omega_L)^3}{6}\left(\frac{\partial^2(1/U)}{\partial\omega^2}\right)_{\omega_L} \cdots$$

The integration near ω_L then gives, after the amplitude A is removed to the left of the integral sign,

$$\frac{1}{2\pi}\,\mathrm{Re}\,A(\omega_L)\exp\left\{i\omega_L\left(t - \frac{x}{W_L}\right)\right\} \times \int \exp\left\{iT'(\omega-\omega_L) - i\,\frac{x}{6}\,(\omega-\omega_L)^3\,\frac{\partial^2(1/U)}{\partial\omega^2}\right\} d\omega$$

This is an integral of the Airy type:

$$\mathscr{A}(\nu) = \int_{-\infty}^{\infty} e^{i(\xi^3 - \nu\xi)}\, d\xi$$

in which

$$\nu = +\,T'\left[\frac{x}{6}\,\frac{\partial^2(1/U)}{\partial\omega^2}\right]^{-1/3}, \qquad \xi = -\frac{T'}{\nu}(\omega - \omega_L)$$

For small values of ν it is easy to calculate an approximate value for this integral.[4]

$$\mathscr{A}(\nu) = \frac{1}{\sqrt{3}}\left[\Gamma\left(\frac{1}{3}\right) + \nu\Gamma\left(\frac{2}{3}\right) - \frac{\nu^3}{18}\Gamma\left(\frac{1}{3}\right) - \cdots\right] \tag{43}$$

$$\Gamma\left(\frac{1}{3}\right) \approx 2.68; \qquad \Gamma\left(\frac{2}{3}\right) \approx 1.354$$

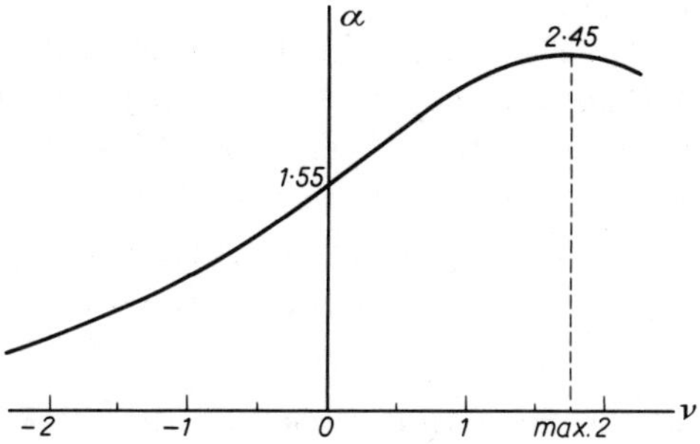

FIG. 7.

The curve in Fig. 7 gives the approximate variation of $\mathscr{A}$ as a function of ν for small values of ν. $\mathscr{A}$ is very small for negative values of ν and has a maximum of about 2.45 for ν about 1.74. Under these conditions, the forerunners have a sizable amplitude given by

$$-\frac{1}{2\pi(\omega_L - \omega_0)}\left[\frac{x}{6}\,\frac{\partial^2(1/U)}{\partial\omega^2}\right]^{-1/3} \mathscr{A}(\nu)\cos\omega_L\left(t - \frac{x}{W_L}\right) \tag{44}$$

If ω_L is not zero, the integration about $-\,\omega_L$ must also be added to this formula.

---

[4] G. Airy, *Trans. Cambridge Phil. Soc.* 8, Part V, p. 593 (1848); L. Brillouin, *Ann. école norm. sup.* **33**, 37 (1916).

This discussion can be summarized as follows. The pure harmonic waves into which the signal has been decomposed are separated from each other. Those waves with frequency ω arrive with group velocity $U(\omega)$ and an amplitude [Eq. (41)] which is directly proportional to $1/(\omega^2 - \omega_0^2)$, which factor enters into formulas (34) and (35) and whose effect is shown in Fig. 6.

At the times t_L (quasi-latent times) defined by Eqs. (42), the forerunners pile up and make a very considerable contribution, with a maximum amplitude of the order of magnitude of

$$\frac{2.45\,\omega_0}{\pi(\omega_0^2 - \omega_L^2)}\left[\frac{x}{6}\,\frac{\partial^2(1/U)}{\partial\omega^2}\right]^{-1/3} \tag{44'}$$

This factor is obtained by superposition of the two expressions (44) corresponding to $\pm\,\omega_1$.

These results are valid only if the absorption is negligible and the phase velocity W does not vary too rapidly with ω. The more exact integration done in the complex plane by the saddle point method confirms these results.

The group velocity U, the velocity of energy transport U_1, and the signal velocity S are practically equal under these conditions.

8. Summary of the Most Important Results; Generalization to Other Types of Waves

This chapter was devoted to a very general discussion of electromagnetic waves in a dispersive medium, and we were very cautious not to introduce any special model. The results obtained can be easily translated for other types of waves, for instance, elastic waves.

In a problem involving transverse elastic waves, we would obtain equations very similar to those of Section 1, but ε would represent the elastic properties and μ would correspond to density. The energy density would be evaluated as in Sections 2 and 3, and formulas similar to Eqs. (20) and (20′) would result. Continuity conditions at a boundary could be worked out as in Section 3, and would be summarized in a formula corresponding to Eq. (22b).

Group velocity U (Section 4) and velocity U_1 for energy transport (Section 5) would be defined in a similar way, and we would arrive at the relation (30). All the results of Section 6 on signal velocity could be repeated.

The reader will find some more examples in Chapter V of L. Brillouin's book *Wave Propagation in Periodic Structures*. (New York: McGraw-Hill Book, 1946; Dover, 1953.) In the next chapter, we will study in more detail the typical model of a dielectric, and compare the results with those of Chapter II.

Literature

Section 1

Lippmann, M., *J. phys.* **9**, 381 (1881).
Boltzmann, L., *Ann. Physik* [2] **155**, 403 (1875).
Pauthenier, M., *Ann. phys.* [9] **14**, 239 (1920); *J. phys.* **5**, 312 (1924); **6**, 1 (1935).
Pellat, H., *J. phys.* **7**, 18 (1898).
Lorentz, H. A., *Encykl. Math. Wiss.* Bd. V, t. 2, cahier 1.
Lienard, A., *Ann. phys.* [9] **20**, 249 (1923).
Brillouin, L., *J. phys.* **6**, 337 (1925).

Section 2

Laue, M., *Ann. Physik* [4] **18**, 523 (1905).

Section 4

Wien, W., *Encykl. Math. Wiss.*, Bd. V, t. 22, No. 28.
Ehrenfest, P., *Ann. Physik* [4] **33**, 1571 (1910).
Also, a large number of classical works.

Section 5

Brillouin, L., *Compt. rend.* **173**, 1167 (1921); "Statistiques quantiques," Chapter I. Presses Universitaires, Paris, 1930.

Sections 6 and 7

Sommerfeld, A., *Ann. Physik* [4] **44**, 177 (1914).
Brillouin, L., *Ann. Physik* [4] **44**, 203 (1914).

CHAPTER V

WAVE PROPAGATION IN A DISPERSIVE DIELECTRIC*

In this chapter we want to specify the properties of a real dielectric and apply to this problem the general formulas of Chapter IV.

1. Formula of Lorentz-Lorenz

In the simplest hypothesis explaining the structure of dielectrics it is assumed that dielectrics are composed of small particles which can be polarized under the influence of an electric field. These particles can be colloidal suspensions, or, for pure materials, they can be molecules or even atoms. In the absence of a field, there is no polarization. One of the following assumptions must be made:

(1). The particles have no permanent electric dipole moment and acquire such a moment only when subjected to a field. This will be the case for atoms or for molecules with homopolar bonds.

(2). Alternatively, the molecules have a permanent dipole moment (heteropolar bonds). In the absence of an external field, these moments are subject to thermal motion which orients them in all directions with equal probability. The average electric moment for a molecule will then be zero, in the absence of a field. In the presence of a field, the molecules tend to orient themselves, and the average dipole moment will no longer be zero.

Let N be the number of particles per unit volume. Each of these particles, when subjected to a field R, acquires an average electric moment γR in the direction of R. The resultant dipole moment per unit volume will then be

$$P = N\gamma R \tag{1}$$

What is the relation between the external field E and the field R to which each molecule is subjected? Each molecule is separated

* See footnote on page 85.

from the next one by an average distance ρ. To a first approximation, the field $\boldsymbol{R}$ (at the point where the molecule is located) can be considered as the field found at the center of a hollow spherical cavity of radius ρ in the midst of a medium having a polarization P. This will be

$$R = E + \frac{4\pi}{3} P \tag{2}$$

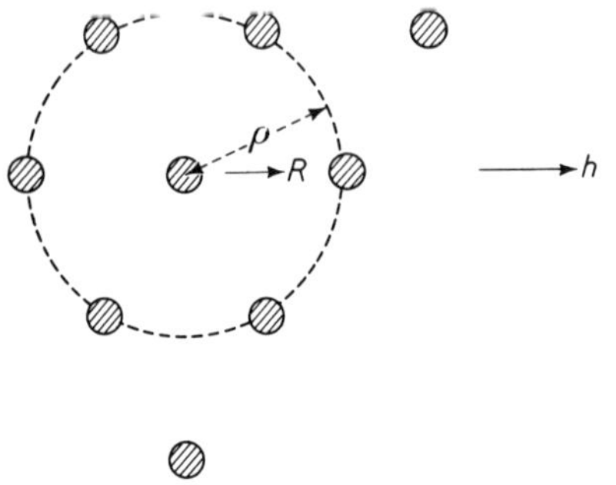

FIG. 1.

This result is independent of the radius ρ, if the polarization $\boldsymbol{P}$ is uniform. The electric displacement D is [1]

$$D = E + 4\pi P = \varepsilon E \tag{3}$$

where ε is the permittivity of the dielectric. Elimination of R and E between these three relations results in

$$\frac{3}{4\pi}\frac{\varepsilon - 1}{\varepsilon + 2} = N\gamma = \mathcal{N}\frac{d}{M}\gamma \tag{4}$$

where $\mathcal{N}$ is Avogadro's number, or the number of molecules per gram mole, M the molecular weight, and d the density of the material under consideration. Formula (4) is called the formula of Lorentz and Lorenz. It shows that $(\varepsilon - 1)/(\varepsilon + 2)$ must be proportional to the density d and to the average polarizability γ of a molecule. This coefficient γ receives contributions of three distinct types (at least to a first approximation):

(1). Electronic polarizability by displacement of the electrons of the atoms.

(2) Ionic polarizability by the spreading apart of the ions of the molecule.

---

[1] From now on the units will be chosen so that the permittivity of free space will be unity.

(3). Dipolar or rotational polarizability, due to the average orientation of the molecules which have a permanent electric dipole moment. This orientation is opposed by the thermal motion of rotation.

In cases (1) or (2), the displacement of the electrons (or ions) is opposed by forces of attraction. Since the moving charges have nonzero masses, there will be one (or several) frequencies of free oscillation in the molecule. The frequencies for type (1) are very high (ultraviolet and visible). Those of type (2) are lower (red or infrared). The rotations of the molecules following (3) are in the far infrared and the radio region. These different orders of magnitude make it possible to distinguish between the above mentioned three types of polarizability.

The reasoning which led to formula (4) contains a number of approximations. It can be predicted that the formula will cease to be applicable in the following cases:

(1). *Large densities:* In this case, the molecules, since they are crowded together, can affect one another by their form and structure, and thus the vibrations will not be described completely by the simplified scheme suggested above. The field due to each individual charge making up the molecule is very complicated at small distances and does not reduce to the field of a dipole unless it is viewed at a sufficiently large distance.

(2). *Molecules of anomalous form:* For molecules in the form of long sticks, it is evident that the above calculations would be inexact. A theory of liquid crystals can be based on these assumptions (Oseen).

(3). *Very high frequencies:* The above calculation assumes that the polarization P is practically constant over a distance of the order of several molecular separations ρ. The reasoning certainly becomes faulty for wavelengths of the order of ρ.

This last situation begins to arise for x-rays if the body considered is in the solid state, or for ultraviolet rays if the body is in the gaseous state. In order to extend the theory to these short wavelengths, the exact structure of the body must be given. Ewald has given a very clear discussion of these problems, which are quite tricky, for different types of crystal structure.

For very small wavelengths (x-rays) a definition of an average dielectric coefficient is no longer possible. The Bragg-Laue selective reflections, which have contributed remarkably to the study of crystal structures, will occur.

It is moreover evident that for very short wavelengths it is unreasonable to apply to the discontinuous medium, the Maxwell equations [Chapter IV, Eqs. (1), (2), and (3)] which are valid for a continuous medium. It is only for wavelengths large compared with the separation between two molecules that the reasoning of Lorentz is correct and that the use of Maxwell's equations is justified. The fine work of Ewald and Born on these questions will not be described here, and the ensuing discussion will be limited to wavelengths from the radio to the visible region for which the Lorentz approximations are valid.

2. Material Medium of Low Density, Consisting of Harmonic Oscillators

For a gas, in which the concentration of molecules is small, the dielectric constant differs only slightly from unity. Formula (4) can then be simplified and rewritten as

$$\varepsilon = 1 + 4\pi N\gamma \tag{5}$$

The atoms or molecules are structures containing electrical charges (electrons or ions). These charges are attracted to their equilibrium positions by forces of mutual attraction [hypotheses (1) and (2) of Section (1)]. A simplified problem in which the molecule is pictured as a harmonic oscillator can be considered as an example, i.e., the problem of a charge e of mass m, characteristic frequency ω_0, and damping factor ρm. If $\mathbf{s}$ is the displacement of the charge, then the equation of motion will be

$$\frac{d^2\mathbf{s}}{dt^2} + 2\rho\frac{d\mathbf{s}}{dt} + \omega_0{}^2\mathbf{s} = \frac{e}{m}\mathbf{E} \tag{6}$$

when the charge is subjected to an external field $\boldsymbol{E}$. (It is to be noted that Eq. (6) is an approximation in that no distinction is made between the fields $\boldsymbol{R}$ and $\boldsymbol{E}$.) When the charge e is at its rest position ($s = 0$) the molecule is not electrified. Thus the dipole moment will be

$$\gamma \boldsymbol{E} = e\boldsymbol{s} \tag{7}$$

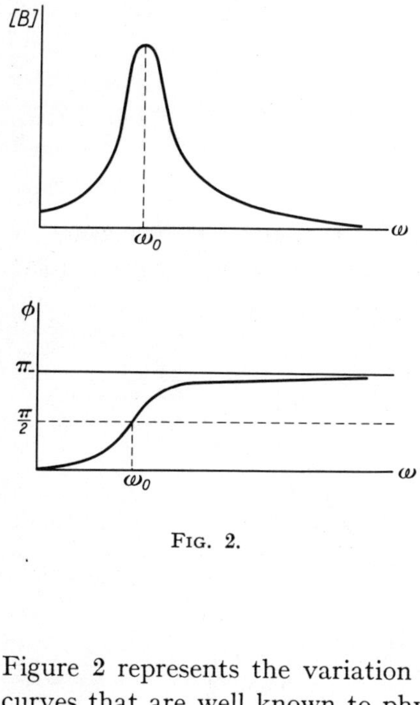

FIG. 2.

One possibility for the field is a sinusoidal variation:

$$E = a \cos \omega t = a \operatorname{Re} e^{i\omega t} \tag{8}$$

A solution of Eq. (6) with a complex amplitude B corresponding to a phase difference ϕ between S and E is:

$$s = \operatorname{Re} (Be^{i\omega t}) \tag{9}$$

$$B(\omega_0^2 - 2i\rho\omega - \omega^2) = a \frac{e}{m},$$

$$B = \frac{a(e/m)}{\sqrt{(\omega_0^2 - \omega^2)^2 + 4\rho^2\omega^2}} e^{i\phi}$$

$$\left(\tan \phi = \frac{2\rho\omega}{\omega_0^2 - \omega^2}\right)$$

Figure 2 represents the variation of $|B|$ and ϕ with ω in resonance curves that are well known to physicists and technicians.

Using Eqs. (5) — (9), one can find the average dielectric coefficient

$$\varepsilon = 1 + \frac{4\pi N\, e^2/m}{\omega_0^2 - 2i\rho\omega - \omega^2} \tag{10}$$

This is a complex number, which means a complex velocity of propagation W. Instead of W, consider the index of refraction n,

$$n = \frac{c}{W} = \sqrt{\varepsilon} = n_r + in_i \tag{11}$$

It has already been noted in the preceding paragraphs, that a complex velocity (or refractive index) signifies that the propagation is accompanied by absorption

$$\exp\left\{-i\omega\left(t-\frac{x}{W}\right)\right\}=\exp\left\{-i\omega\left(t-\frac{n_r x}{c}\right)-\frac{n_i\omega x}{c}\right\}$$

$$=\exp\{-\kappa x\}\exp\left\{-i\omega\left(t-\frac{n_r x}{c}\right)\right\} \tag{12}$$

with a coefficient of absorption

$$\kappa=\frac{\omega}{c}n_i \tag{13}$$

The real part of the index of refraction is useful for calculating the differences of phase between two points which are a distance x apart. Thus, c/n_r actually plays the role of *phase velocity.*

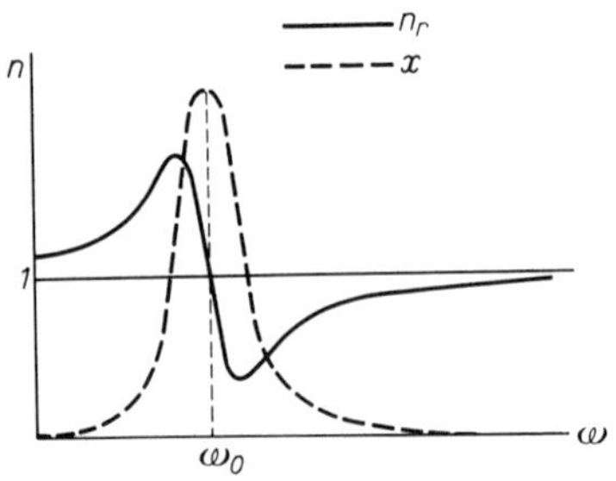

FIG. 3.

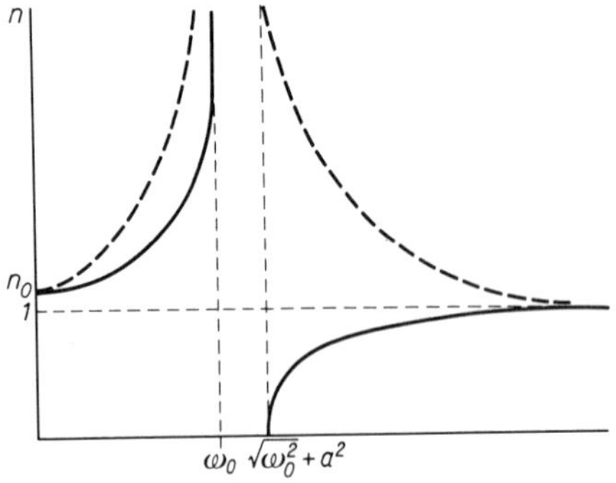

FIG. 4. Key: ———, $n = c/W$ where W = phase velocity; – – – –, c/U where U = group velocity.

Figure 3 shows how the index of refraction n_r and the coefficient of absorption κ vary near the resonance ω_0. The curve for the index n_r crosses the line $n = 1$ near ω_0 and varies rapidly near there. The steepness of this slope is closely related to the sudden variation of the phase ϕ, shown in Fig. 2. The absorption κ is directly related to the amplitude $|B|$ of the oscillations of the elementary oscillators.

At frequencies far from ω_0 the imaginary terms can be neglected and then

$$\varepsilon \approx 1 + \frac{a^2}{\omega_0{}^2 - \omega^2} \qquad \left(a^2 = 4\pi N \frac{e^2}{m}\right)$$

$$n = \frac{c}{W} = \sqrt{\varepsilon} \qquad (\kappa = 0) \tag{14}$$

$$\frac{c}{U} = n + \omega \frac{dn}{d\omega}$$

The curves of Fig. 4 indicate the nature of the results obtained with these asymptotic formulas.

3. Propagation of the Waves in the Medium

First of all, the exact nature of the waves in the above mentioned medium will be studied, taking the absorption into account.

A wave propagating in the x direction can be written as

$$E_z = a e^{i\omega(t - x/W)}, \qquad H_y = A e^{i\omega(t - x/W)} \tag{15}$$

If a is real, then A will be complex, indicating that there is a phase difference between these two vectors. Maxwell's equations (with ε complex) require that

$$\frac{A}{W} = \varepsilon a, \qquad \frac{a}{W} = \mu_0 A, \qquad \varepsilon \mu_0 W^2 = 1 \tag{16}$$

Let $\tilde{A}$ denote the complex conjugate of A. The preceding equations then give

$$\tilde{\varepsilon} \mu_0 \tilde{W}^2 = 1, \qquad |\varepsilon| \mu_0 |W|^2 = 1, \qquad \frac{\tilde{A}}{\tilde{W}} = \tilde{\varepsilon} a$$

The intensities of the electric and magnetic fields are related by

$$\mu_0 |A|^2 = \mu_0 A \tilde{A} = \frac{a\tilde{A}}{W} = \frac{\tilde{\varepsilon}\tilde{W}}{W} a^2 = \frac{a^2}{\mu_0 W \tilde{W}} = \frac{a^2}{\mu_0 |W|^2} = |\varepsilon| a^2 \tag{17}$$

but,

$$|\varepsilon| = 1 + 4\pi N \frac{e^2}{m}\left(\frac{1}{\omega_0{}^2 - 2ip\omega - \omega^2}\right) = 1 + \frac{4\pi N\, e^2/m}{\sqrt{(\omega_0{}^2 - \omega^2)^2 + 4p^2\omega^2}}$$

What is the energy density in the medium through which the wave is propagating? This can be found by adding together the energies of the electric and magnetic fields (in the vacuum between the atoms) and the potential and kinetic energies of the N oscillators.

$$(18) \qquad \mathscr{E} = \frac{\varepsilon_0}{8\pi}\overline{E^2} + \frac{\mu_0}{8\pi}\overline{H^2} + N\left(\frac{1}{2}\, m\overline{\dot{s}^2} + \frac{1}{2}\, m\, \omega_0{}^2\overline{s^2}\right)$$

This relationship then leads, by virtue of the relations (9) and (17), and after setting $\varepsilon_0 = 1$ as in the previous two sections, to

$$(19) \qquad \mathscr{E} = \frac{\overline{E^2}}{8\pi}\left[1 + |\varepsilon| + 4\pi N\frac{e^2}{m}\frac{\omega^2 + \omega_0{}^2}{(\omega_0{}^2 - \omega^2)^2 + 4p^2\omega^2}\right] = \varepsilon_1\frac{\overline{E^2}}{4\pi}$$

A coefficient ε_1 can be defined, as in Chapter IV, Eqs. (20) and (20′); the expression for it, derived from Eqs. (17) and (18), will be *real* and equal to

$$\varepsilon_1 = 1 + 2\pi N\frac{e^2}{m}\left[\frac{1}{\sqrt{(\omega_0{}^2 - \omega^2)^2 + 4p^2\omega^2}} + \frac{\omega_0{}^2 + \omega^2}{(\omega_0{}^2 - \omega^2)^2 + 4p^2\omega^2}\right]$$

(20)

The expression obtained in Chapter IV, Section 3, is no longer applicable here, since there is absorption. The role of the residual energy $\mathscr{E}_0$ at the time when the electric field is zero can be clearly seen. This notion was introduced in Eqs. (13), (14), and (17) of Chapter IV in a somewhat arbitrary manner. From Eq. (18) it is seen that at the time when the electric field E is zero, the magnetic field H is not zero, because of the phase difference between the two. The potential energy of the oscillators is small, but their kinetic energy is very important. These several terms enter into $\mathscr{E}_0$.

In order to avoid any error, the laws of refraction must also be rewritten. As at the end of Section 3, Chapter IV, the discussion will be restricted to the case of normal incidence.

$$\begin{array}{lll} & \text{Incident wave:} \quad E_z = a \; e^{i\omega(t - x/c)} & H_y = A \; e^{i\omega(t - x/c)} \\ (21) & \text{Refracted wave:} \quad E_z = a' \; e^{i\omega(t - x/W)} & H_y = A' \; e^{i\omega(t - x/W)} \\ & \text{Reflected wave:} \quad E_z = a'' e^{i\omega(t + x/c)} & H_y = A'' e^{i\omega(t + x/c)} \end{array}$$

If a' is real, then A' is complex as in Eq. (15). Similarly, a, A, a'' and A'' are complex. The conditions of refraction, Eq. (22) of Chapter IV require that

$$a + a'' = a', \qquad A - A'' = A' \tag{22}$$

but,

$$A = \frac{a}{\mu_0 c}, \qquad A'' = \frac{a''}{\mu_0 c}, \qquad A' = \frac{a'}{\mu_0 W}$$

The second relation in Eq. (22) can thus be written as

$$a - a'' = \frac{c}{W'} a' = na'$$

where n = complex index of refraction.

From these various relations, it is easy to derive that

$$a = \alpha + i\beta, \qquad a'' = a' - \alpha - i\beta$$

$$-a' + 2\alpha + 2i\beta = na' = (n_r + in_i)a'$$

and

$$|a|^2 - |a''|^2 = \alpha^2 - (a' - \alpha)^2 = a'(-a' + 2\alpha) = n_r a'^2 \tag{23}$$

This last relation replaces formula (22) of Chapter IV.

4. The Velocities U, U_1, and S in the Medium

The next point to consider is the effect of absorption on the group velocity U, the velocity of energy transport U_1, and the signal velocity S. Far from the resonance region (ω very different from ω_0) the absorption is negligible, and the imaginary parts of ε and the index of refraction n can be neglected. Then the asymptotic formulas (14) can be used. It is almost obvious that this case is the same as the cases treated in Sections 2 and 7 of Chapter IV and that the velocities U, U_1, and S are identical. This point will be verified by using the complete formulas.

The *group velocity* U was defined by formula (27) of Chapter IV where the real part of $1/W$ must be used. This can be written in the form

$$\frac{c}{U} = \frac{d(n_r\omega)}{d\omega} = n_r + \omega\frac{dn_r}{d\omega} \tag{24}$$

In Fig. 2, the curve for the variation of n_r is drawn. It is then easy to construct graphically the curve for c/U. This curve presents a curious anomaly in the absorption band. c/U can become less than 1, and even less than zero. This means that the group velocity U can be greater than the velocity of light c, can be infinite and even negative! These results are sufficient to show that, in this region, the group velocity no longer represents the velocity of a signal or of energy transport.

Far from the absorption band, formulas (14) give

$$\begin{aligned} \frac{c}{U} &= n_r\left(1+\omega\frac{d\log n_r}{d\omega}\right) \approx n\left(1+\frac{\omega}{2}\frac{d\log\varepsilon}{d\omega}\right) \\ &\approx n\left[1+\frac{4\pi Ne^2}{\varepsilon m}\,\frac{\omega^2}{(\omega^2-\omega_0{}^2)^2}\right] \end{aligned} \tag{25}$$

The real part of c/U is always less than the value of Eq. (25). The latter is, as can be seen, always greater than n_r and infinite at ω_0.

The *velocity* U_1 *of energy transport* can be gotten from Chapter IV, formulas (22a) and (29) which gave relation (30). According to the calculations of the preceding sections, Eq. (22a) of Chapter IV is replaced by Eq. (23), and Eq. (29) of Chapter IV retains the same form if absolute values are used. Thus equation (30) of Chapter IV becomes

$$\varepsilon_1 U_1 = cn_r, \qquad \frac{c}{U_1} = \frac{\varepsilon_1}{n_r} \tag{26}$$

ε_1 has been calculated in (20). Far from the absorption band these formulas show that

$$\frac{c}{U_1} = \frac{n}{\varepsilon}\,\varepsilon_1 = \frac{n}{\varepsilon}\left[1 + \frac{2\pi Ne^2}{m}\left(\frac{1}{\omega_0{}^2 - \omega^2} + \frac{\omega_0{}^2 + \omega^2}{(\omega_0{}^2 - \omega^2)^2}\right)\right]$$

$$(27) \qquad = \frac{n}{\varepsilon}\left(1 + \frac{4\pi Ne^2}{m}\,\frac{\omega_0{}^2}{(\omega_0{}^2 - \omega^2)^2}\right)$$

$$= n\left(1 + \frac{4\pi Ne^2}{\varepsilon m}\,\frac{\omega^2}{(\omega_0{}^2 - \omega^2)^2}\right)$$

after making use of (14). Thus U and U_1 are the same, since formulas (25) and (27) are equal.

In the absorption band, ε_1 follows a regular variation and has a pronounced maximum near ω_0. This can immediately be seen from Eq. (20). Formula (26) thus shows that c/U_1 follows an analagous variation with a distinct maximum in this dangerous region. The velocity U_1 thus decreases greatly in this anomalous region and passes through a minimum. It is quite different from the group velocity U.

The signal velocity S is defined as in Section 6 of Chapter IV, and requires a detailed discussion of the integral (36), in which W is a complex velocity. Since this was discussed in detail in Chapter III it is enough to give the results here. The velocity S is found to equal the group velocity U, except in the region of absorption. In this region, *it is very difficult to define a signal velocity precisely*, since the signal arrives very gradually without a distinct front. The c/S curve in Fig. 5 was calculated from a certain definition of the front, but, depending on the sensitivity of the detector, any value between S and U_1 could be found. The curve of U_1 approaches, moreover, the curve U, having the form shown in Fig. 4, if the absorption is neglected. One result, at least, is clear: the velocity of the front of the signal cannot exceed the velocity c. The first forerunners travel through the medium in which all the oscillators are still at rest, since no wave has as yet hit them. These oscillators are only gradually set into motion as the various forerunners hit them. But nothing can propagate faster than c.

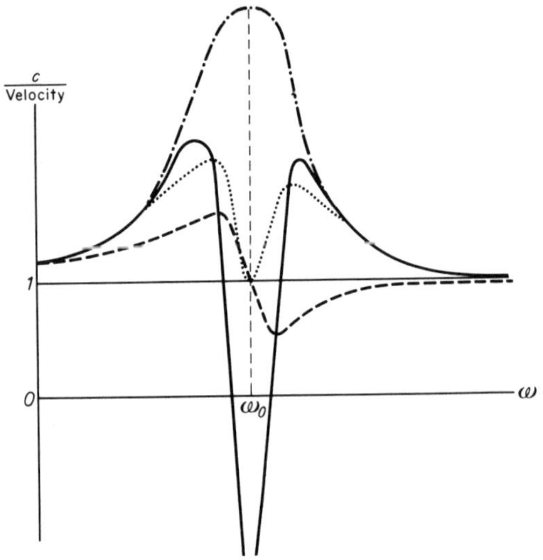

FIG. 5. Key: – – – –, c/W where W = phase velocity;
———, c/U where U = group velocity;
· · · ·, c/S where S = signal velocity;
· — · —, c/U_1 where U_1 = velocity of energy transport.

5. The Forerunners

Consider a signal of frequency ω far different from ω_0. The main part of the signal arrives with the signal velocity S which is nearly equal to the group velocity. What about the forerunners? For those forerunners which have frequencies far from ω_0, the discussion of Section 7 of Chapter IV applies. Thus, a series of forerunners are to be expected, each starting with those frequencies at which the group velocity is stationary (maximum or minimum).

Using Fig. 3, one can see that outside the absorption region, the *group velocity* is a *maximum* for:

Infinite frequencies $\quad U_\infty = c$

Zero frequencies $\quad U_0 = W_0 = \dfrac{c}{\sqrt{1 + \dfrac{4\pi N e^2}{m\omega_0{}^2}}}$

Thus, a *first group of forerunners* will arrive with velocity c and will be composed of very high frequencies. The exact nature of these forerunners is given by formula (41) of Section 7, Chapter IV.

$$\frac{2\omega_0}{\omega^2 - \omega_0{}^2} \frac{\cos\left\{\omega\left(t - \frac{x}{W}\right) + \frac{\pi}{4}\right\}}{\sqrt{-2\pi x \frac{\partial(1/U)}{\partial\omega}}} = \frac{\omega_0}{a\omega^2}\sqrt{\frac{2c\omega^3}{\pi x}} \cos\left\{\omega\left(t - \frac{x}{W}\right) + \frac{\pi}{4}\right\}$$

(28)

Since for very high frequencies

$$a^2 = \frac{4\pi N e^2}{m}, \qquad \varepsilon \approx 1 - \frac{a^2}{\omega^2}, \qquad \frac{c}{W} \approx 1 - \frac{a^2}{2\omega^2}$$

$$\frac{c}{U} \approx 1 + \frac{a^2}{2\omega^2}, \qquad -\frac{\partial(c/U)}{\partial\omega} \approx \frac{a^2}{\omega^2}$$

On the other hand, for stationary phase, ω and t are related by condition (39), see Chapter IV.

$$t - \frac{x}{U} = t - \frac{x}{c} - \frac{a^2 x}{2c\omega^2} = T - \frac{a^2 x}{2c\omega^2} = 0$$

with

$$T = t - \frac{x}{c}$$

whence

$$\omega\left(t - \frac{x}{W}\right) = \omega\left(t - \frac{x}{c} + \frac{a^2 x}{2c\omega^2}\right) = 2\omega T = a\sqrt{\frac{2xT}{c}}$$

since

$$\omega = a\sqrt{\frac{x}{2cT}}$$

Introducing these values into Eq. (28), and carrying out some simple manipulations, we obtain the result:

$$\text{(29)} \qquad \frac{\omega_0}{\sqrt{\pi}\, a^{3/2}} \left(\frac{2c}{x}\right)^{3/4} T^{1/4} \cos\left\{a\sqrt{\frac{2xT}{c}} + \frac{\pi}{4}\right\}$$

which is valid when T is not too small. This result is confirmed by a more exact analysis,[2] which takes the damping constant ρ into account. The only modification in Eq. (29) for the first forerunners is a factor $e^{-2\rho T}$ which is equal to 1 for very small T but thereafter decreases the amplitude of the forerunners considerably.

Now, *the second group of forerunners* is characterized by very low frequencies. The calculations for these will be done only very briefly. The result, after making the suitable approximations, is

$$\varepsilon = 1 + \frac{a^2}{\omega_0{}^2}\left(1 + \frac{\omega^2}{\omega_0{}^2} + \ldots\right) = \left(1 + \frac{a^2}{\omega_0{}^2}\right)\left[1 + \frac{a^2\omega^2}{\omega_0{}^2(a^2 + \omega_0{}^2)} + \ldots\right]$$

$$n = n_0 + A\omega^2, \qquad n_0 = \sqrt{1 + \frac{a^2}{\omega_0{}^2}}, \qquad A = \frac{a^2}{2\omega_0{}^3\sqrt{a^2 + \omega_0{}^2}}$$

$$\frac{c}{U} = n_0 + 3A\omega^2$$

$$\frac{\partial(c/U)}{\partial\omega} = 6A\omega \quad \text{is positive,} \quad \frac{\partial^2(c/U)}{\partial\omega^2} = 6A$$

Since the derivative of $1/U$ is positive, it is necessary to observe the changes of sign in formula (41) of Section 7, Chapter IV. The relation between ω and t is given by Eq. (39), of Chapter IV.

$$t - \frac{x}{U} = t - \frac{xn_0}{c} - \frac{3A\omega^2 x}{c} = T' - \frac{3A\omega^2 x}{c} = 0$$

with

$$T' = t - \frac{xn_0}{c}$$

whence

$$\omega\left(t - \frac{x}{W}\right) = \omega\left(T' - \frac{A\omega^2 x}{c}\right) = \frac{2}{3}\,\omega T' = \frac{2}{3}\,(T')^{3/2}\sqrt{\frac{c}{3Ax}}$$

---

[2] See Chapter III, Eq. (20a).

Formula (41) of Chapter IV, with the suitable changes of sign, is written as

$$\frac{2\omega_0}{\omega_0^{\,2} - \omega^2} \frac{\cos\left[\omega\left(t - \frac{x}{W}\right) - \frac{\pi}{4}\right]}{\sqrt{2\pi x \frac{\partial(1/U)}{\partial\omega}}}$$

$$(30) \qquad = \frac{\omega_0}{\omega_0^{\,2} - \frac{cT'}{3Ax}} \frac{1}{\sqrt{\pi}} \left[\frac{c}{3AxT'}\right]^{1/4} \cos\left\{\frac{2}{3} T'^{3/2} \sqrt{\frac{c}{3Ax}} - \frac{\pi}{4}\right\}$$

This is the equation for the second forerunners which arrive a little later than the first ones and start at $T' = 0$. This result agrees with the more exact calculation which take the damping coefficient ρ,[3] neglected in Eq. (30), into account.

The forerunners [Eq. (30)] have an important characteristic, namely, that they begin at $T' = 0$ with a rather large amplitude which decreases bit by bit afterwards. Formula (30) actually would give an infinite amplitude at $T' = 0$, but it loses its validity for this time. The exact form of the start of the signal has been calculated in Eq. (44), Chapter IV, Section 7 and is given by an Airy function $\mathscr{A}(\nu)$ (Fig. 7). Formula (44) of Chapter IV reduces to

$$(31) \qquad \frac{1}{2\pi\omega_0} \left(\frac{c}{Ax}\right)^{1/3} \mathscr{A}(\nu) \qquad (\omega_L = 0)$$

with

$$\nu = -T' \left(\frac{c}{Ax}\right)^{1(3}$$

using Eqs. (42), (43), (44) of Chapter IV and Eq. (30) above.

Several orders of magnitude will serve to illustrate these results. Using a yellow incident signal, which travels one centimeter through a medium whose characteristic frequency is in the ultraviolet, the numbers are

$$x = 1 \text{ cm.}, \qquad \omega = 4 \times 10^{15} \quad (\lambda = 0.5\mu), \qquad \omega_0 = 4 \times 10^{16}$$

---

[3] See Chapter III, Eq. (19b).

If the index of refraction n is 1.5, this gives

$$n^2 = 1 + \frac{a^2}{\omega_0{}^2 - \omega^2}, \qquad a^2 = 1.24\,\omega_0{}^2, \qquad A \approx \frac{1}{5} \times 10^{-33}$$

The *first forerunners* arrive with the velocity c of light in vacuum. They require a time $\frac{1}{3} \times 10^{-10}$ sec. to travel 1 cm. Their original amplitude is zero. After a time $T = 10^{-12}$ after the start of these forerunners, their amplitude has a magnitude around

$$\frac{\omega_0}{\sqrt{\pi}\, a^{3/2}} (2c)^{3/4}\, T^{1/4} \approx 10^{-3.5}$$

using Eq. (29), which means an intensity around 10^{-7} compared with that of the actual signal.

For the *second forerunners,* the start is given by Eq. (31). The Airy function has a maximum value of about 2.45 and thus, using the above orders of magnitude, the initial amplitude is about $\frac{1}{2} \times 10^{-2}$, or the relative intensity is $\frac{1}{4} \times 10^{-4}$. As the time T' increases, these forerunners decrease slowly, according to Eq. (30). After a time T' of 10^{-12} the amplitude has decreased to 10^{-3} or a relative intensity of 10^{-6}, and is already very weak.

The front of these second forerunners may possibly be observable!

6. A Real Transparent Medium, Having Several Absorption Bands

Actual materials have more than one absorption band, and thus have several characteristic frequencies $\omega_0, \omega_0{}', \ldots,$ so that the dielectric constant is given by a sum of terms such as Eq. (10),

$$n^2 = \varepsilon = 1 + \sum_k \frac{a_k{}^2}{\omega_{0k}^2 - 2i\rho_k\omega - \omega^2} \tag{32}$$

The curves of the index of refraction $n = c/W$ and of c/U (U = group velocity) have the form shown in Fig. 6, where the case of a medium with two characteristic frequencies ω_0 and $\omega_0{}'$ has been sketched. The results for this case will be analagous to those of the preceding sections. Far from the absorption bands, the velocities U, U_1, and S

will coincide. For each absorption band, the velocities will be equivalent to those shown in Fig. 5, the signal velocity being then ill-defined and having any value between U_1 and S, depending on the sensitivity of the detector.

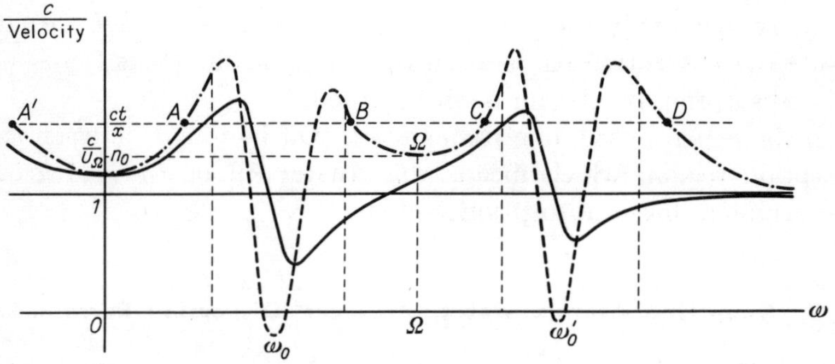

FIG. 6. Key: ———, c/W where W = phase velocity;
·—·—, c/U where U = group velocity (part of the usable curve outside the absorption bands);
— — — —, c/U (parts which are unusable, situated in the absorption bands).

The nature of the forerunners can also be read directly from these curves. The *forerunners with velocity* c will still exist, being the first to arrive and having very high frequencies. They will be given by a formula like Eq. (29). The *forerunners of velocity* c/n_0 and very low frequencies will also occur, represented by a formula similar to Eq. (30). But also, a *third group of forerunners* will be found, corresponding to those frequencies Ω between ω_0 and ω_0' with an incoming velocity $U_{n'}$, which, for the case shown in the figure, is less than the velocity c/n_0 of the zero frequency forerunners. But there is nothing which shows *a priori* that this is a general condition. At the frequency Ω, the group velocity has a maximum (quasi-latent time). The form of the corresponding forerunners would be found by using formulas (44) and (44′) of Chapter IV, and summing the contributions for $+\Omega$ and $-\Omega$.

At a time t, the system of forerunners is obtained by superposition of the frequencies whose group velocity U is equal to x/t. A line parallel to the ω axis can be drawn at the height ct/x which cuts the curve c/U at the points A,B,C,D, and at the symmetric points A',B',C',D'.

This gives a superposition of four forerunners of different frequencies, which interfere with each other. The frequencies situated inside the absorption bands are suppressed so that, for predicting the forerunners, only the parts (· — · — · —) of the curve c/U situated outside the absorption bands need be used, and the parts (———) in the absorption bands can be disregarded.

In the general case, one frequency Ω will be found between each absorption region, which means that there will be $(n + 1)$ groups of forerunners for n absorption regions.

7. Quantized Atomic States, Kramers' Dispersion Formula

An actual material medium possesses a certain number of characteristic frequencies for emission and for absorption. This is the empirical fact which Section 2 tried to account for by considering each atom as a harmonic oscillator with a characteristic frequency ω_0. Actually, it is now well-known that such a model is just a gross approximation. The atomic structure is a separate world obeying special mechanical laws, those of quantum theory. The atom can exist in a series of states, with energies

$$E_0, E_1, \ldots E_i, \ldots E_k, \ldots$$

each of which is stable to some extent. While the atom is in one of these states, it does not emit any radiation. Emission or absorption occurs only when the atom jumps from one state E_i to another E_k, and the frequency ν of the emitted radiation is then given by Bohr's relation, which contains the quantum contant h;

$$h\nu_{ik} = E_i - E_k \qquad (\omega = 2\pi\nu) \tag{33}$$

During the transition time, the atom may be regarded as a sort of harmonic oscillator of frequency ν_{ik} and the amplitude q_{ik} of these vibrations can be calculated. The square of this magnitude $|q_{ik}|^2$ is a measure of the intensity of the radiation of frequency ν_{ik}. If

q_{ik} represents emission of light associated with a transition $i \to k$, then q_{ki} represents absorption of light in a transition $k \to i$. These two quantities are complex conjugates, so that $|q_{ik}|^2 = |q_{ki}|^2$. Thus, a strong emission line for $(i \to k)$ corresponds to a strong absorption for $(k \to i)$.

If, now, a ray of light of frequency ν is incident on a medium composed of quantized atoms, what will happen?

Each atom will be the source of secondary rays of the same frequency as the incident radiation, but with different phases. This is the *coherent* radiation, which corresponds to the effect studied in Section 2 from the classical point of view. This coherent radiation adds to the incident radiation to form the refracted wave. The index of refraction n is given by a famous formula of Kramers,

$$(34) \qquad n^2 - 1 = \frac{4\pi N e^2}{m} \sum_j \frac{f_{jk}}{\omega_{jk}^2 - \omega^2}$$

This formula is quite analagous to that of classical theory [Eq. (32)]. Here, there are no damping factors ρ included, but this is due to the approximations made in the theory. A more exact application of quantum theory would result in introducing the quantum equivalent of ρ.

The numbers f_{jk} are directly proportional to the amplitudes q_{jk} of the various characteristic frequencies. If q_{jk} is the amplitude for the direction of the electric field of the incident wave, and y_{jk} is the amplitude for the direction of propagation, then

$$(35) \qquad f_{jk} = \frac{8\pi^2 m}{h} \nu_{jk} y_{jk} q_{jk} = \frac{4\pi m}{h} \omega_{jk} y_{jk} q_{jk}$$

Kramers' formula (34) calls for several remarks. If the atoms are all originally in their normal state E_k with minimum energy, all the frequencies ω_{jk} are absorption lines corresponding to the possible transitions to states of higher energy E_j. Then formula (34) corresponds exactly to the classical equivalent (32).

It is however possible, that the atoms will be found in an excited state E_k, i.e., not in their state of lowest energy. Then, in Eq. (34), not only the frequencies for *absorption* from E_k to states of higher energy than E_k, will occur but also the frequencies of *emission* corresponding to transition from E_k to states E_j with less energy than E_k. By virtue of formulas (35) and (33), the coefficients f_{jk} for emission will be *negative,* while those for absorption are positive.

This peculiarity cannot occur in the classical formula (32), since the frequencies of absorption and emission are identical there. Classically, the frequencies were assumed to be independent of the initial energy E_k of the atom.

Finally, the coefficients f_{jk} are directly proportional to q_{jk}. Thus, the only frequencies ω_{jk} which are effective in Kramers' formula are those which are actually found in the spectrum of the atom. There are forbidden transitions $j \rightarrow k$ (noncombining levels), for which the corresponding amplitude is always zero. These transitions also will contribute no terms to the dispersion formula (34).

Thus, the Kramers' formula makes it possible to apply the classical results with practically no changes. The frequencies which are observed are those given by the energy differences (33). The frequencies of the electrons in their orbits (as in the old model of Bohr) are never observed.

Beside the coherent radiation which has the same frequency as the incident wave, the atoms can emit an *incoherent* radiation, or can even be ionized and emit *secondary* electrons. The incoherent radiation has a different frequency than the incident wave. If ν is the incident frequency and ν_{jk} one of the characteristic frequencies of the atom, then the emitted radiation will have frequencies $\nu \pm \nu_{jk}$. This change of frequency is typical of the phenomena predicted by the theory of Kramers, Heisenberg, and Smekal, and discovered experimentally by the noted Indian physicist Raman. Furthermore, if there is much absorption, i.e., if the frequency ν is near one of the characteristic frequencies ν_{jk} of the atom, then a certain number of frequencies $\nu_{j'k'}$ of the atom can be emitted. These result from the fact that if the atom is initially in the state E_k, then by absorbing a quantum of energy it undergoes a transition to a higher state E_j and in returning to the normal state E_k, it can emit different frequencies. If the frequency ν is very high, then it may even ionize the atom, ejecting one or more electrons (photoelectric effect). Finally, for very small wavelengths (x- or γ-rays), the Compton effect can also occur.

These several effects are mentioned here only for the purpose of putting Kramers' dispersion formula into the correct context, and to show how it can be distinguished from the other optical effects.

8. The Relation Between the Problem Treated and the Analogous Technical Problems

It is believed that the previous discussion contains the essential facts on the subject of the propagation of waves in material media. The existence of dispersion and characteristic frequencies of the medium introduces, as has been shown, some serious complications, and leads to very delicate mathematical problems.

A large number of researchers have attacked these problems in the last few years, because the problem treated here is closely connected to very important technical problems. First of all, there are the problems posed by the propagation of radio waves in the *Heaviside layer*, and by the reflections of those radio waves which can be observed. The Heaviside layer is assumed to be situated in the upper atmosphere and to consist of ions and free electrons. These free charges result in a medium with a characteristic frequency $\omega_0 = 0$, and the propagation of radio waves in this medium is very similar to the problem treated here.

If the damping constant ρ is neglected (it is very small for free charges), then the curves of Fig. 4 will look like the ones in Fig. 7. The coefficient

$$a = \sqrt{4\pi N(e^2/m)}$$

is directly related to the number N of free electrons per cubic centimeter. Waves with frequencies ω less than a cannot propagate; they are absorbed. For $\omega = a$, the phase velocity W is infinite and the group velocity is zero, so that the oscillatory energy remains stationary, i.e., is not propagated. As the frequency ω increases, the waves are propagated with a still small group velocity, which gradually increases.

A complete theory must include the effect of damping; this can be done by inserting a suitable damping factor ρ. Then, a velocity of energy transport U_1 will be obtained (shown as the dotted curve in the right part of Fig. 7). This velocity has very small values (c/U_1 is very large) in the region between 0 and a. This qualitative result can easily be obtained also by examining the curves of Fig. 5.

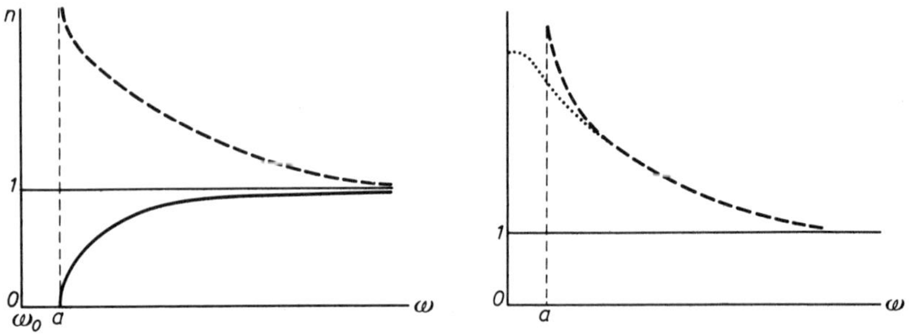

FIG. 7. Key: ———, $n = c/W$ where W = phase velocity;
– – – –, c/U where U = group velocity;
····, c/U_1 where U_1 = velocity of energy transport.

The velocity U_1 and the signal velocity S coincide with the group velocity U for those frequencies ω far from a. In the region between 0 and a there will be a curve similar to that in Fig. 5. However, as has already been stated, the definition of a signal velocity is very difficult in the absorption region. It seems that the velocity S given in Fig. 5 is actually too high, and that the curve for U_1 represents a more reasonable estimate. Thus, for the very low frequencies ($\omega \leqslant a$), the signal velocity will be very small, but not zero.

The evaluation of the signal velocity has been discussed thoroughly by Baerwald, who uses a method of integration in the complex plane which is more exact than the one used previously by the author. The result is a curve for c/S which has a very sharp maximum in each absorption region. This curve for c/S is very close to the curve c/U_1 shown in Fig. 5. One of the curves calculated by Baerwald is given here. In Fig. 8, the curve for c/S evaluated by the method used by the author is shown (lower curve, clearly, a lower limit) and also the asymptotic curve of Baerwald[4] upper curve, upper limit).

[4] For the units used and a detailed discussion, refer to the paper by H. Baerwald, *Ann. Physik* 7, 731 (1930).

Depending on the sensitivity of the detector used, any value between these curves could be found.

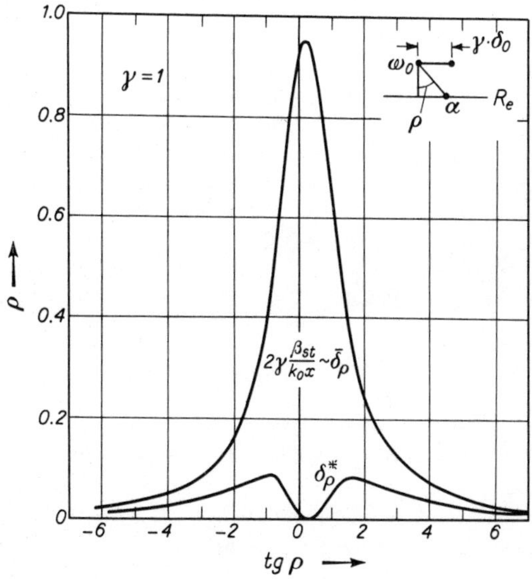

FIG. 8. Brillouin's curve (lower limit) and asymptotic curve (upper limit) for the inverse of the signal velocity in a region of selective absorption.

Very similar problems are also encountered in the propagation of telephonic or telegraphic signals. Loaded transmission lines, filters, and lines produce problems of the same type which are of very great practical interest. The existence of substantial forerunners is a source of great annoyance for transmissions. They result in a repetition of the signal (artificial echo) which is often intolerable in practice. All these problems are treated by the general methods outlined here. Their connection with the subject matter covered in this chapter is mentioned, even though no discussion of these problems will be given.

Literature

Section 1

Oseen, C. W., *Kgl. Svenska Vetenskapsakad. Handl.* **61**, No. 16 (1921); **63**, No. 1 (1922); *Arkiv Mat. Astron. Fysik,* fifteen articles published between 1923 and 1931, Vols. **18** to **22A**; *Fortschr. Chem. Physik u. physik. Chem.* **2**, No. 2 (1929).

Ewald, P. P., *Thesis*, Munich, 1912; *Physik. Z.* **14**, 465 (1913); *Fortschr. Chem. Physik u. physik. Chem.* **18**, No. 8 (1925); "Sommerfeld Festschrift," p. 134. Hirzel, Leipzig, 1929. Lectures at the Poincaré Institute, 1932.

Born, M., "Dynamik der Kristallgitter." Teubner, Leipzig, 1915. "Probleme der Atomdynamik." Springer, Leipzig, 1926.

Errera, J., "Polarisation diélectrique." Presses Universitaires, Paris, 1928.

Debye, P., "Handbuch der Radiologie," Vol. 5. Akademische Verlagsges., Leipzig, 1924.

Sections 2, 3 and 4

Brillouin, L., "Statistiques quantiques," Chapter I and Appendix I. Presses Universitaires, Paris, 1930. The results given at this point, Appendix I, are not quite accurate.

Sections 5 and 6

On the saddlepoint integration and integration in the complex plane, see:

Debye, P., *Math. Ann.* **67**, 535 (1909); *Sitzber. bayer. Akad. Wiss. Math.-naturw. Kl.* (1910).

Brillouin, L., *Ann. école norm. sup.* **33**, 17 (1916).

Also, works by H. G. Baerwald indicated below in the literature on Section 8.

Section 7

Kramers, H. A., *Nature* **113**, 673 (1924); **114**, 310 (1924); *Physica* **5**, 369 (1925).

Kramers, H. A., and Heisenberg, W., *Z. Physik* **31**, 681 (1925).

Born, M., Jordan, P., Heisenberg, W., *Z. Physik* **35**, 557 (1926).

Brillouin, L., *J. phys.* **7**, 135 (1926).

Sommerfeld, A., "Atombau, Wellenmechanik," Ergänzungsband, pp. 193–202. Vieweg, 1929.

Klein, O., *Z. Physik* **41**, 407 (1927).

Schrödinger, E., "Abhandlungen zur Wellenmechanik." Leipzig, 1927. Also, most textbooks on Quantum mechanics.

Section 8

Baerwald, H. G., *Ann. Physik* [5] **6**, 295 (1930); **7**, 731 (1930); **8**, 565 (1931); *Elek. Nachr.-Tech.* **7**, 331 (1930).

Campbell, G. A., *Bell System Tech. J.* November (1922).
Carson, J. R., "Operatorenrechnung." Springer, 1929.
Cauer, W., *Arch. Elektrotech.* **17**, No. 4 (1926); *Sitzber. preuss. Akad. Wiss. Physik.-math. Kl.* **33** (1927); *Elek. Nachr.-Tech.* **6**, 272 (1929).
Edler, H., *Arch. Elektrotech.* **23**, 1 (1929).
Elert, D., *Ann. Physik* [5] **7**, 65 (1930).
Forsterling, K., "Lehrbuch der Optik." Hirzel, 1928.
Forster, R. M., *Bell System Tech. J.* April, June (1924).
Hoyt, R. S., *Bell System Tech. J.* **3**, 414 (1924).
Kupfmüller, K., *Elek. Nachr.-Tech.* **1**, 141 (1924); **5**, 18 (1928); *Wiss. Veröffentl. Siemens-Werken* **5**, 51 (1926).
Lewy, E., *Physik. Z.* **31**, No. 8 (1930).
Mason, W. P., *Bell System Tech. J.* **6**, 258 (1927).
Meyer, U., *Z. tech. Phys.* **2**, 306 (1921).
Pollaczek, F., *Elek. Nachr.-Tech.* **1**, 80 (1924); **2**, 197 (1925); *Z. tech. Phys.* **9**, 265 (1928); *Ann. Physik* [5] **2**, 991 (1929).
Sommerfeld, A., *Ann. Physik* [4] **81**, 1153 (1926).
Stewart, G. W., *Phys. Rev.* **20**, 528 (1922); **25**, 90 (1925).
Strecker, F. and Feldkeller, R., *Wiss. Veröffentl. Siemens-Werken* **8**, No. 2, 70 (1929); *Elek. Nachr.-Tech.* **6**, 93 (1929).
Wagner, K. W., *Arch. Elektrotech.* **2**, 315 (1915); **4**, 172 (1916); **8**, 61 (1919); *Elek. Nachr.-Tech.* **5**, 1 (1928).
Wallot, F., *Wiss. Veröffentl. Siemens-Werken* **2**, 189 (1922).
Weyl, H., *Ann. Physik* [4] **60**, 481 (1919).
Zobel, J., *Bell System Tech. J.* **2**, (1923).

CHAPTER VI

WAVES IN WAVE GUIDES AND OTHER EXAMPLES

1. Guided Waves

Guided waves provide an excellent example for the distinctions between phase, group, signal, or energy velocities which we shall discuss in the present chapter. The electromagnetic theory of these waves was discussed extensively by Sommerfeld,[1] who showed how the phase velocity always exceeds the velocity of light in vacuum c; actual wave propagation occurs, for each mode, on frequencies above the *cut-off* frequency for which the phase velocity is infinite. The point we want to emphasize is the fact that all other velocities (especially the group velocity) are below the velocity of light. We shall use a very simple discussion, which applies particularly well for rectangular wave guides, and provides a clear physical explanation of these properties.[2]

2. Acoustic Waves

The problem of sound vibrations in hollow pipes was studied theoretically many years before the corresponding electromagnetic problem, notably by Lord Rayleigh[3] in 1897. Probably because of experimental difficulties, the importance of his results was not appreciated at the time. They were not experimentally verified until much later, after accurate methods and appropriate equipment for wave generation and detection (loudspeakers and microphones) had become available.

---

[1] A. Sommerfeld, "Electrodynamics," Sections 22–25, especially pp. 193–197. Academic Press, New York, 1952.

[2] L. Brillouin, *Rev. gén. elec.* **40**, 227 (1936), quoted in reference 1.

[3] Lord Rayleigh, "Theory of Sound," Vol. 2. 1897.

As in other ways, Lord Rayleigh was much ahead of his time. Interest in ultrahigh frequencies revived an interest in acoustic waves, and the earlier experimental studies were repeated in refined form, allowing for the observation of all the higher modes[3,4] of waves predicted by Lord Rayleigh.

For a sound wave in air, it can be shown that the velocity potential f satisfies the wave equation

$$\Delta f - \frac{1}{C^2}\frac{\partial^2 f}{\partial t^2} = 0 \tag{1}$$

where C is the natural velocity of sound in free air, Δ is the Laplacian operator

$$\Delta = \nabla^2 = \frac{\partial^2}{\partial x^2} + \frac{\partial^2}{\partial y^2} + \frac{\partial^2}{\partial z^2}$$

and the displacement velocity of the air particles is given by

$$V = \operatorname{grad} f$$

that is,

$$v_x = \frac{\partial f}{\partial x}, \qquad v_y = \frac{\partial f}{\partial y}, \qquad v_z = \frac{\partial f}{\partial z}$$

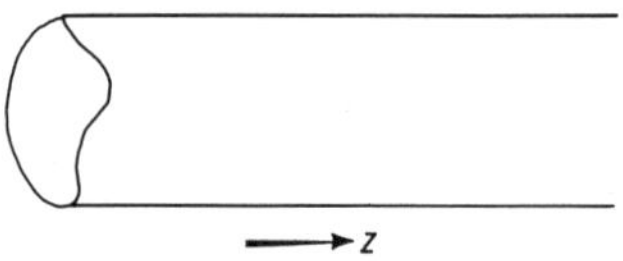

FIG. 1.

Consider now a wave travelling in the z direction down a cylindrical tube or pipe (Fig. 1) and try for a solution of the form

$$f(x,y,z,t) = \phi(x,y)\, e^{i(\omega t - kz)} \tag{3}$$

the exponential factor giving the propagation in the z direction, and ϕ giving the transverse variation of amplitude.

The velocity in the pipe is the phase velocity $\omega/k = W$, and the wave length in the pipe is $\Lambda = 2\pi/k$.

Substitution of this form of solution into the differential equation gives us an equation for ϕ:

$$\frac{\partial^2\phi}{\partial x^2} + \frac{\partial^2\phi}{\partial y^2} + \left(\frac{\omega^2}{C^2} - k^2\right)\phi = 0 = \underset{xy}{\Delta}\phi + K^2\phi \tag{4}$$

---

[4] H. E. Hartig and C. E. Swanson, *Phys. Rev.* **54**, 618 (1938).

with

$$K^2 = \frac{\omega^2}{C^2} - k^2$$

The solution of this equation will be given by certain functions of x and y which involve K. If the walls of the tube are rigid, there can be no velocity perpendicular to the wall, that is

$$v_n = \frac{\partial f}{\partial n} = 0 \tag{5}$$

where n is a normal to the side wall of the tube, or

$$\frac{\partial \phi}{\partial n} = 0$$

This cannot be true for *any* solution of Eq. (4), but may be possible for the proper values of K. We find (as will be clearer when we consider a little later the particular case of a rectangular pipe) that these values of K form a double infinity which we call the *characteristic* or *proper values* K_{nm}, and the corresponding solutions $\phi(x,y,K_{nm})$ are the proper functions ϕ_{nm}.

For a drum or membrane, we have an equation of the same type, where ϕ is then the displacement itself, and where K is a multiple of ω, the proper values thus giving directly those frequencies at which the membrane can vibrate and still satisfy the boundary conditions.

In our case, ω is not given directly, and does not form a discrete set. It is only limited by the condition that K be one of the K_{nm}:

$$K_{nm}^2 = \left(\frac{\omega^2}{C^2} - k^2\right) \tag{6}$$

according to Eq. (4), or

$$\omega^2 = C^2(k^2 + K_{nm}^2)$$

so that for a given *mode of vibration* (n,m), there is a lowest possible frequency, the *critical frequency* ($k = 0$, or $\Lambda = \infty$):

$$\omega_{\text{crit}} = CK_{nm} = \omega_{nm} \tag{7}$$

The (n,m) mode $\phi_{nm}\, e^{i(\omega t - kz)}$ is damped out for all frequencies below this value. Hence the tube acts as a high pass filter. Note that the sound velocity in the pipe is greater than its velocity C in free air.

$$W = \frac{\omega}{k} = C\left(1 + \frac{K_{nm}^2}{k^2}\right)^{1/2} \tag{8}$$

or,

$$\left(\frac{C}{W}\right)^2 + \left(\frac{\omega_{nm}}{\omega}\right)^2 = 1 \tag{9}$$

which result is shown in Figs. 2, 3, and 4.

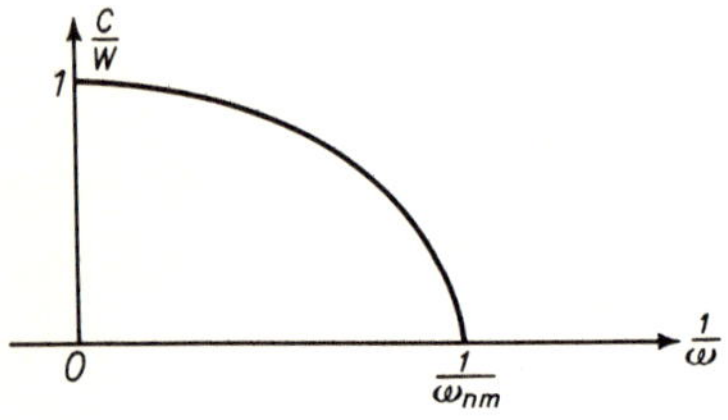

FIG. 2.

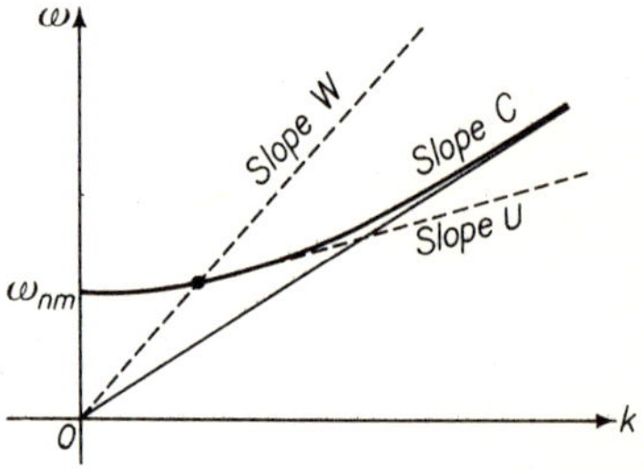

FIG. 3.

The group velocity U is given by

$$U = \frac{d\omega}{dk}$$

and since

$$\omega^2 = k^2C^2 + \omega_{nm}^2$$

we have

$$\omega d\omega = kC^2 dk$$

and

$$U = \frac{kC^2}{\omega} = \frac{C^2}{W}$$

or

$$UW = C^2 \tag{10}$$

so that

$$W > C, \qquad U < C$$

It is easy to show that for frequencies below cut-off one obtains attenuation instead of propagation along the pipe.

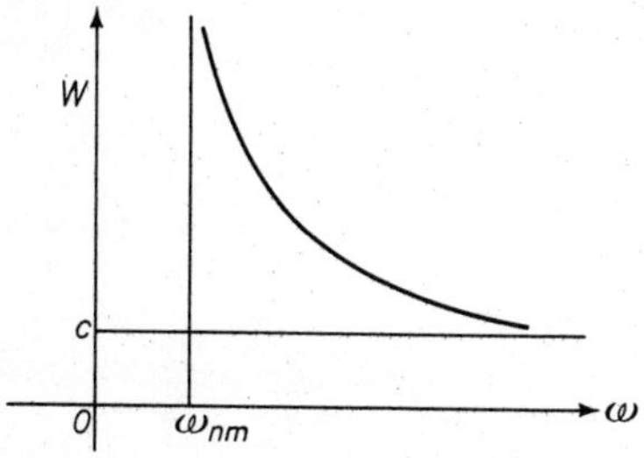

FIG. 4.

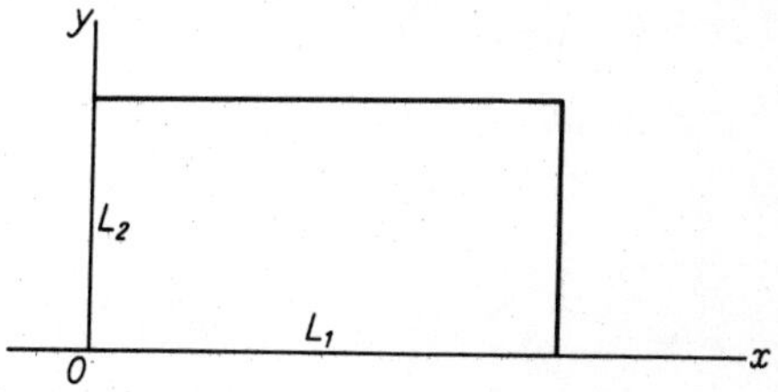

FIG. 5.

3. Rectangular Tube

In the case of the rectangular pipe (Fig. 5), the condition that there be no velocity normal to the walls gives us the boundary condition

$$\frac{\partial \phi}{\partial x} = 0 \qquad \text{at } x = 0,\ L_1$$

$$\frac{\partial \phi}{\partial y} = 0 \qquad \text{at } y = 0,\ L_2$$

and the function ϕ must satisfy Eq. (4).

The possible functions ϕ are therefore

$$\phi_{nm} = X_n Y_m = A_{nm} \cos \frac{n\pi}{L_1} x \cos \frac{m\pi}{L_2} y \tag{11}$$

with

$$K_{nm}^2 = \pi^2\left[\left(\frac{n}{L_1}\right)^2 + \left(\frac{m}{L_2}\right)^2\right] = \frac{\omega^2}{C^2} - k^2 \tag{12}$$

The resulting wave is

$$f = A_{nm} \cos \frac{n\pi}{L_1} x \cos \frac{m\pi}{L_2} y \, e^{i(\omega t - kz)}$$

The elementary solution $(nm) = 00)$ is

$$f_{00} = \phi_{00} \, e^{i(\omega t - kz)}$$

Now let us see how the different modes vary in the cross section. For the (0, 1) solution, the term $\cos (\pi/L_2)y$ shows that there is a node $(f = 0)$ at

$$\frac{\pi}{L_2} y = \frac{\pi}{2}$$

or $y = \frac{1}{2} L_2$. And, similarly, the mode (10) has a node at $x = \frac{1}{2} L_1$.

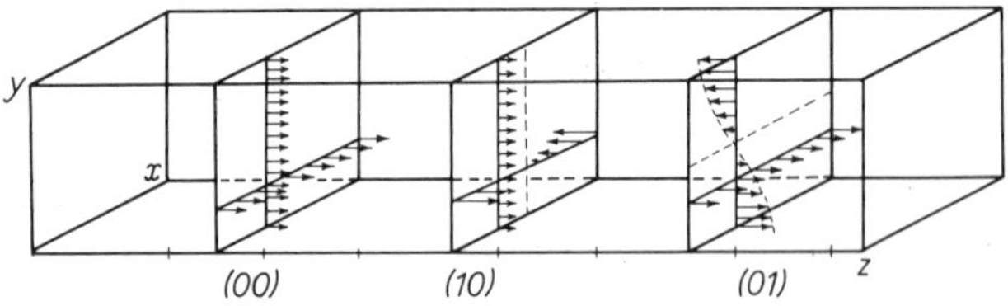

FIG. 6.

More generally, the (n,m) mode exhibits n nodes in the x direction and m nodes in the y direction as sketched in Fig. 6.

4. Physical Significance of Guided Waves

The waves in a pipe can propagate only a long certain modes of vibration, and they exhibit a *phase velocity* W larger than the sound velocity C in free space.

The shape of the wave results from the reflecting boundaries of the pipe. Let us consider a rectangular pipe open at one end (Fig. 7) with a wave falling obliquely on its bottom surface.

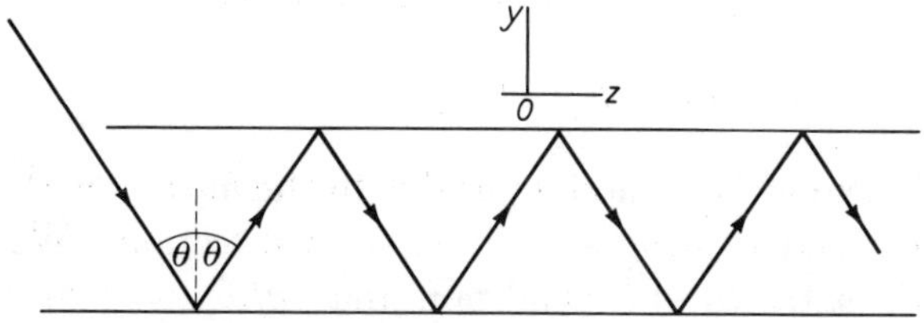

FIG. 7.

This structure will reflect the wave over and over again, so that the velocity of sound along the new, zigzag path is still C, but the velocity U at which the signal actually progresses down the pipe is much slower, in fact we see that $U = C \sin \theta$. And W is the phase velocity of the interference patterns set up by the incident and reflected waves. To see that this latter is the case, let us superpose the two waves, as shown in Fig. 8.

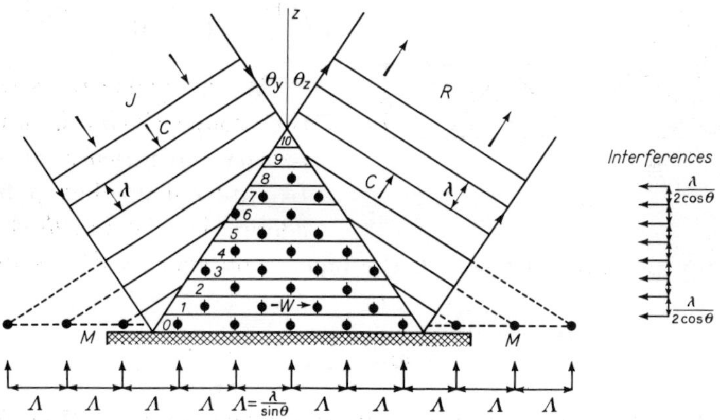

FIG. 8. An incident wave J is falling upon a mirror M and reflected along R. Interference fringes build up in the region where both waves J and R are superimposed. A series of dark fringes, numbered 0,1,2,. . . 10 are parallel to the mirror; between these dark fringes the superposition results in new waves, with a wave length $\Lambda > \lambda$ and a velocity $W > C$.

If the incident wave has its normal in the direction $(0, -k_2, k_3)$, the reflected wave must be in the direction $(0, k_2, k_3)$, so that the sum of the two is

$$f = Ae^{i[\omega t - (-k_2 y + k_3 z)]} + Ae^{i[\omega t - (k_2 y + k_3 z)]} \tag{13}$$
$$= 2A \cos (k_2 y) e^{i(\omega t - k_3 z)}$$

which is a system of fixed nodes parallel to the mirror, with amplitude between nodes constituting a wave in the z direction. We see that f automatically satisfies the condition that $\partial f/\partial y = 0$ at the mirror surface. We also have $\partial f/\partial y = 0$ in the parallel planes $k_2 y = m\pi$, or

$$y = \frac{m\pi}{k_2} \; (m = 0,1,2 \ldots)$$

so that a second mirror could be placed at any one of these planes without disturbing the motion.

A second mirror at $y = (m + 1)\pi/k_2$ yields our previous solution $(0, m)$. The physical picture shows that

$$\frac{U}{C} = \frac{C}{W} = \sin \theta \tag{14}$$

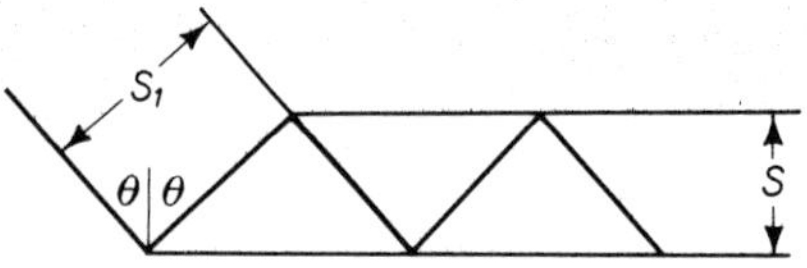

Fig. 9.

We now wish to show that the group velocity U and the *velocity of transfer of energy* U_{en} are equal. Let ρ be the energy density and Φ the flux of energy per cm.^{2} per sec. in the pipe. The velocity U_{en} is defined by

$$\Phi = \rho U_{en}$$

If Φ_1 is the flux in the incident free wave, we have (Fig. 9) and energy density $\rho_1 = A^2$ in the incident wave

$$S_1 = 2S \sin \theta \tag{15}$$
$$\Phi_1 S_1 = \Phi S$$

Now, the energy density is measured by $|f^2|$. Hence,

$$\Phi_1 = \overline{f_1{}^2}\, C = \rho_1 C = A^2 C$$

$$\Phi = \overline{f^2}\, U_{en} = 4A^2\left(\frac{1}{2}\, U_{en}\right)$$

since $\cos^2 k_2 y = \frac{1}{2}$.

And so,

$$\Phi_1 S_1 = A^2 C(2 \sin \theta) = \Phi S = 2A^2 U_{en} S$$

or

(17) $$U_{en} = C \sin \theta = U$$

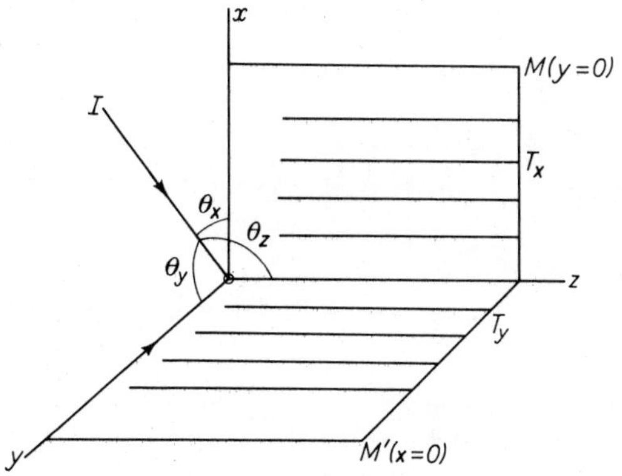

Fig. 10. An incident beam I falls upon two mirrors M and M' at right angles. The lines T_J and T_3 show the position of black fringes parallel to both mirrors

Now let us consider an incident wave not parallel to the yz plane, so that there will also be reflection from a mirror in this plane. That is, consider a wave with normals in any direction (k_1, k_2, k_3).

(18) $$f_1 = A e^{i(\omega t - k_1 x - k_2 y - k_3 z)}$$

This will be reflected from a mirror in the xz plane (Fig. 10) in the direction $(k_1, -k_2, k_3)$, and we have, as wave of superposition, remembering that $\partial f/\partial y = 0$ at $y = 0$, as before:

(19) $$f_2 = 2A \cos k_2 y \; e^{i(\omega t - k_1 x - k_3 z)}$$

progressing now in the (k_1, k_3) direction instead of in the z direction.

But this wave is in turn reflected on the yz plane $x = 0$, giving for the wave of superposition, noting that $\partial f/\partial x = 0$ at $x = 0$:

$$f = 4A \cos k_1 x \cos k_2 y \, e^{i(\omega t - k_3 z)} \tag{20}$$

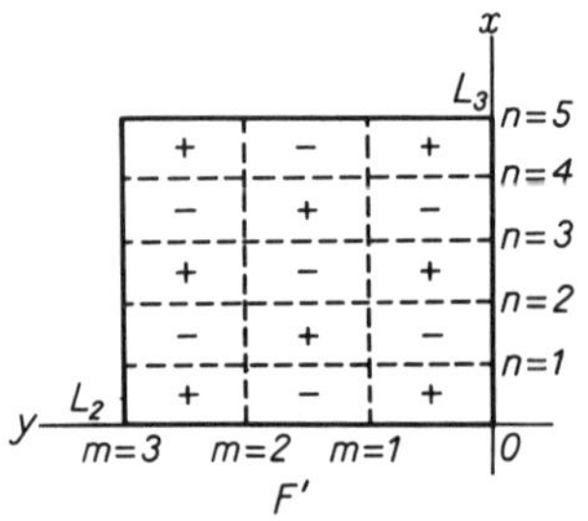

FIG. 11. Distribution of positive and negative vibrations in the cross section of a rectangular pipe ($n = 5$, $m = 3$).

or the (nm) solutions on proper choice of k_1 and k_2: $k_1 = n\pi/L_1$ and $k_2 = m\pi/L_2$. Fig 11 shows the distribution of vibrations in a cross-section.

5. Electromagnetic Guided Waves

Results very similar to the preceding ones may be obtained for electromagnetic waves propagating along a pipe. We shall consider a metallic pipe and simplify the problem by assuming the metal's conductivity to be infinite. Within the pipe, electromagnetic waves follow Maxwell's equations. Let us call z a coordinate taken along the pipe and x and y two cartesian coordinates in the cross-section. We assume all fields to depend upon z and t by an exponential

$$e^{i(\omega t - kz)} \tag{21}$$

which indicates propagation along the pipe.

We may discuss the solution to Maxwell's equations for this case in a way analogous to that in which we treated the acoustic case, looking for propagation down the tube. We find that E_z and H_z satisfy the equations

$$\begin{aligned} \underset{xy}{\Delta} E_z + K^2 E_z &= 0 \\ \underset{xy}{\Delta} H_z + K^2 H_z &= 0 \end{aligned} \tag{22}$$

with the other components E_x, E_y, H_x, H_y expressed in terms of E_z and H_z, respectively. The conditions at the boundary are $E_z = 0$, $\partial H_z/\partial n = 0$.

Two important types of solution are the *electric type* ($H_z = 0$, $E_z \neq 0$, i.e., *transverse magnetic*, or TM), and the *magnetic type* ($E_z = 0$, $H_z \neq 0$, i.e., *transverse electric*, or TE).

As in the acoustic case, we find the relation similar to Eqs. (6) and Eq. (8):

$$K^2 = \omega^2\left(\frac{1}{C^2} - \frac{1}{W^2}\right) \tag{23}$$

and again

$$UW = C^2, \qquad W > C, \qquad U < C$$

However, the (00) solution no longer exists.

For the H-waves, we have the same boundary condition, $\partial H/\partial n = 0$, as in the acoustic case, and hence the same solution, which for a rectangular pipe is:

$$H_z = \cos\frac{n\pi x}{L_1}\cos\frac{m\pi y}{L_2}\, e^{i(\omega t - kz)} \tag{24}$$

For the E-wave, the boundary condition is $E_z = 0$, and hence the solution is, for a rectangular pipe,

$$E_z = \sin\frac{n\pi x}{L_1}\sin\frac{m\pi y}{L_2}\, e^{i(\omega t - kz)} \tag{25}$$

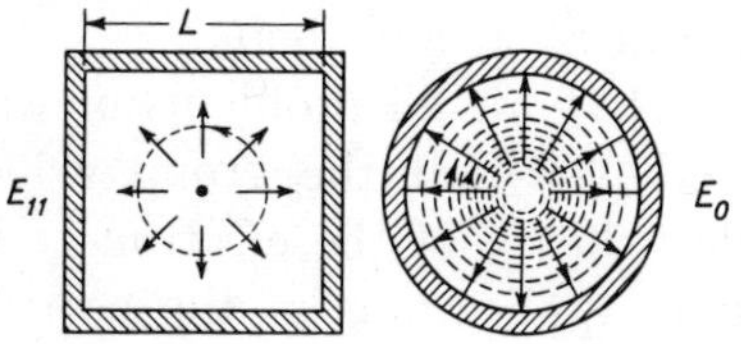

FIG. 12.

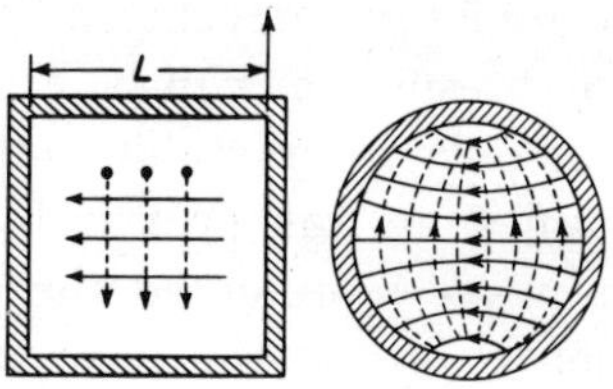

FIG. 13.

Figures 12 and 13 indicate the distribution of electric and magnetic lines of forces in the cross-section for some typical waves: solid lines correspond to electric lines of forces and dotted lines represent magnetic lines of forces. Figure 12 shows, on the left, a pipe of square cross-section enclosing a wave E_{11}, while on the right there is a pipe of circular cross-section in which the fields correspond to the so-called E_0 solution. The similarity of the two waves is easily recognized. Figure 13 shows two similar H_{01} solutions for a square or a circular pipe.

6. Some Other Typical Examples

There is hardly any problem of wave propagation where the preceding definitions would not play an important role. Group, signal, and energy velocities have always to be defined, in addition to the usual phase velocity. A variety of such examples was given in another book by the author.[5] The one-dimensional problem is first discussed for a variety of discrete structures, and the definition of group, signal, and energy velocities is given in Chapter V, where it is also proven that the energy velocity is directly related to the "characteristic impedance" of the system. Chapter VI discusses problems in two dimensions, and Chapter VII deals with three-dimensional structures and discusses the zone structure. The general results obtained for mechanical vibrations and waves can easily be extended to any kind of waves propagating in periodic structures. Electronic ψ-waves in a crystal lattice have exactly similar properties, and the zone structure is of great importance for them. Group velocity for the ψ-waves corresponds directly to electron-particle-velocity, and this correspondence explains all the peculiar properties of electrons in metals or in semiconductors. The whole theory of electrons in semiconductors developed by Shockley is based entirely on the author's results, as can be easily seen in Shockley's book.

Not only in crystalline structures, but for all problems of wave-mechanics, it was proven by Schrödinger that the group velocity of the wave represented the particle velocity of the electrons. This relation is one of the most important applications of the notion of group velocity.

---

[5] L. Brillouin, "Wave Propagation in Periodic Structures." First edition, McGraw-Hill, New York, 1946; second edition, Dover, New York, 1953. French edition, with M. Parodi as coauthor: "Propagation des ondes dans les milieux périodiques." Masson, Paris, 1956.

AUTHOR INDEX

Books Published by L. Brillouin

Masson & Cie, Paris

"Cours de physique théorique: Les tenseurs en mécanique et en élasticité." 1st edition, 1937; 2nd edition, 1949, one volume, 370 pages.

"Notions élémentaires de mathématiques pour les sciences expérimentales." 1st edition, 1935; 2nd edition, 1938; 3rd edition, 1947, one volume, 284 pages.

"Propagation des ondes dans les milieux périodiques" (with M. Parodi). 1956, one volume, 347 pages.

"La Physique et la théorie de l'Information." 1959, one volume, 325 pages.

Presses Universitaires, Paris

"La théorie des quanta et l'atome de Bohr." 1923, 1 volume, 181 pages (out of print).

"La théorie des quanta, I." (2nd edition.) L'atome de Bohr; la mécanique analytique et les quanta; les spectres de multiplets. 1931, one volume, 364 pages.

"La théorie des quanta, II." (2nd edition.) Les statistiques quantiques et leurs applications. 1930, two volumes, 404 pages.

Gauthier-Villars, Paris

Influence de la température sur l'élasticité d'un solide. *Mémorial des Sciences Mathématiques.* No. 99 (1940), 65 pages.

"Jubilé de M. M. Brillouin pour son 80ème anniversaire." 1935, one volume, 440 pages.

"Jubilé scientifique de M. M. Brillouin, allocutions." 1935, one volume, 40 pages.

Chiron, Paris

"Les mesures en haute fréquence" (with H. Armagnat). 1923, one volume, 200 pages (out of print).

Hermann, Paris
Actualités scientifiques et industrielles

No. **15** Les statistiques quantiques et leur application aux électrons libres dans les métaux, 1930, 44 pages.

No. **39** Notions de mécanique ondulatoire, les méthodes d'approximation. 1932, 35 pages.

No. **59** La diffraction de la lumière par les ultrasons. 1933, 32 pages.

No. **71** La méthode du champ self-consistent. 1933, 47 pages.

No. **88** Les électrons dans les métaux, du point de vue ondulatoire. 1934, 35 pages.

No. **89** Conductibilité électrique et thermique des métaux. 1934, 75 pages.

No. **159** Les champs self-consistents de Hartree et de Fock. 1934, 37 pages.

No. **160** L'atome de Thomas-Fermi et la méthode du champ self-consistent. 1934, 46 pages.

No. **549** La structure des corps solides dans la physique moderne. 1937, 53 pages.

Albin-Michel, Paris

"La vie, la matière et la théorie de l'Information." 1959, one volume, 246 pages.

Springer, Berlin

"Quantenstatistik" (Struktur der Materie, Volume XIII). 1931, one volume, 530 pages.

Russian Edition of "Quantum Statistics," 1931.

Blackie & Son, London

"Selected Papers on Wave Mechanics" (with L. de Broglie). 1928, one volume, 150 pages.

McGraw-Hill, New York

"Wave Propagation in Periodic Structures." 1946, one volume, 247 pages.

Dover, New York

"Wave Propagation in Periodic Structures," 2nd edition. 1953, 255 pages.

Academic Press, New York

"Science and Information Theory." 1956, one volume, 320 pages.

"Wave Propagation and Group Velocity" (with A. Sommerfeld). 1959, one volume, 154 pages.